MW00366240

NAME

Fortune Hotel →

Induction service form

pǝʇsᴉʍꓕ Travel Stories

Fortune lǝʇoH

Sarah Champion :ɹoʇᴉpƎ

HAMISH HAMILTON LTD

Published by the Penguin Group
Penguin Books Ltd, 27 Wrights Lane, London W8 5TZ, England
Penguin Putnam Inc., 375 Hudson Street, New York, New York 10014, USA
Penguin Books Australia Ltd, Ringwood, Victoria, Australia
Penguin Books Canada Ltd, 10 Alcorn Avenue, Toronto, Ontario, Canada M4V 3B2
Penguin Books (NZ) Ltd, Private Bag 102902, NSMC, Auckland, New Zealand

Penguin Books Ltd, Registered Offices: Harmondsworth, Middlesex, England

First published by Hamish Hamilton 1999
1 3 5 7 9 10 8 6 4 2

Artwork by Ashworth/Sissons – STILL

Set in 9.5/12.5pt Monotype Helvetica 45 Light
Typeset by Rowland Phototypesetting Ltd, Bury St Edmunds, Suffolk
Printed in Great Britain by Clays Ltd, St Ives plc

A CIP catalogue record for this book is available from the British Library

ISBN 0-241-14043-9

Twisted Travel Stories

Fortune Hotel

Editor: Sarah Champion

Contents

Editor:

Sarah Champion

Welcome to the Fortune Hotel

Sarah Champion was born in Manchester in 1970. She is the editor of three anthologies, Shenanigans, Disco 2000 and Disco Biscuits, the influential collection of writings from the chemical generation. She is

currently travelling.

I noticed my first Fortune Hotel amidst the neon tack of Chinese restaurants as we headed out of Ho Chi Minh city on Vietnam's Route 1. I liked the name. I wanted to stop. I wanted to stay there. We didn't have time. 'Fortune Hotel, where you roll a dice to decide your future,' I smiled to myself as I gambled with my life on the back of a strange boy's Honda, our destination uncertain. *Fortune Hotel*. The words were so poetic, evoking images of last dollars and chance encounters that could change your life.

That night I lay in bed, hypnotized by the geckos zig-zagging across the ceiling and the slow clank of the ceiling fan. Fortune had taken me to an obscure town in the Mekong Delta where all the hotels are owned by the communist authorities. The power had cut out while we waited in reception for our passports to be handed in at the police station; the entire town had been thrown into darkness. The dour concierge led us irritably up the stone steps to our rooms, his candle illuminating a rat scuttling into a corner.

'Fortune Hotel,' I laughed, trying to ignore the biting bedbugs, the red ants climbing into my wash-bag, the inch-long cockroaches in the shower, the mosquitoes and sewage smells rising from the river below to fill the room. Fortune was not this hotel's real name, but it would have suited it. After all, fortune can be bad as well as good. This was the best hotel in town. It was the *only* hotel in town.

Later I discovered that there are many Fortune Hotels all over the globe, all unrelated, from a five-star luxury tower in Bangkok to an eerie dive in Cambodia's capital Phnom Penh. There are others in Manila, Taiwan's capital Taipei,

Ahmadabad, Singapore and the St Petersburg district of Florida.

Meanwhile, that night in the Mekong, as I lay awake in the unbearable heat wondering what the hell I was doing there, the idea for this book germinated. There is nothing in the guidebooks that can capture the strangeness of times like these. And nothing in the travel-writing sections of bookshops either, their shelves filled with thirtysomething tales of vineyards in the South of France; stories of elephant trekking, cycling up mountains, rock-climbing, lost tribes, the Raj, the Silk Route – twee travel novels with oil paintings or water-colours on their jackets. Most travel-writing seems stuck in some colonial time-warp, written by middle-aged men in linen suits.

There are a few exceptions – notably Alex Garland's *The Beach*, Howard Marks's *Mr Nice* and William Sutcliffe's *Are You Experienced?* These are bestsellers in the second-hand bookshops of Bangkok's Khao San Road, where all backpackers pass at some time, selling or exchanging books to lighten their load.

Fortune Hotel takes things a step further, with some of the world's most interesting writers getting closer to the truth of travelling than ever before: the alienation and loneliness, the sickness and boredom, the aimlessness and the surreality – occasionally, too, the fun.

Santiago, Marseilles, Jodhpur, Kazakhstan, East Berlin, Jaisalmer, Karachi, Tel Aviv, Kathmandu, Vienna, Bethlehem, Nepal . . . the destinations blur, as does the line between fact and fiction. Some stories are true, others invented.

Fortune Hotel is a hallucinogenic rotation of airport lounges, runways, sleazy guest-houses, bus stations, beach resorts and bars. The characters are travelling to escape, to rekindle relationships, to forget the past or to erase themselves. They search for enlightenment, adventure or oblivion. They make drug deals, go to football matches, take dead-end holiday jobs and taxi rides through alien cities or drink alone. Sometimes they wear inappropriate clothes and behave obnoxiously to the locals. Amidst strange smells and exotic tongues they try to remember who they are and why they're there.

And before you check in with the first story, remember to abide by the 'hotel rules', as stated on a faded photocopy in that seedy room in Vietnam: 'No narcotic or erotic or politik in rooms. Please leave all gun, explosiffs and knife at reception.'

PROTECTED - AREA

VISAS

VISAS

VISA NOT VALID FOR ANY

Martyn Bedford
A Representative in Automotive Components

GORAKH

Second Secretary (Passport)

LONDON (U. K)

Martyn Bedford was brought up in south London but now lives in Yorkshire. He worked as a journalist for a number of years but gave up to write full-time with the success of his first novel Acts of Revision, which won the Yorkshire Post Best First Novel Award. He has published two other novels, Exit, Orange & Red and The Houdini Girl, which is published by Penguin. His previous books have been

translated into nine languages.

My Cousin is Kissing

On the approach to Jodhpur, Nathan went into the WC and bolted the door. He gave himself a moment to attune to the motion of the train. The sickness wasn't fully upon him, then, but there were the beginnings of a headache, a queasiness, a sense of his body recoiling from itself. He unfastened his flies and eased the moneybelt out. The fabric was tidemarked with damp. He pulled a parcel from the smaller of the two zippered compartments, examining the integrity of the polythene bag and the tape that sealed it. A camera hung from his neck. He took it from its case and popped the back. Removing the film, he pressed the parcel into the cavity behind the lens and moulded the contents so that the flap would click shut again. Done. He tidied his clothes. Composed himself. This was OK, he could handle this. He weighed the secret of what he held within the camera and the knowledge impressed him with its potency. Back in his seat, he evaded a smile of incipient conversation from the passenger opposite. Outside, dirt-tracks gave way to streets, shanties to squat cubes of white, the buildings glinting in amplification of the day's brilliance. Jodhpur materialized like a city sculpted from salt.

He took an auto-rickshaw – too tired to walk, too jaded to breach the touts picketing the station concourse. Unwashed, unshaven, unslept; stiff from sitting for so long on bare wood. His skeleton had absorbed every vibration of the ten-hour journey, transmuting general discomfort into a full pulse of pain at the base of his spine. The arrival was familiar: odours of sewage and burnt ghee; cars, cycles, mopeds, buses, trucks and auto-rickshaws reeling by on fast-forward, patterning the air with beige dust, din and petrol fumes. On seething pavements, the men wore white and the women were swathed in psychedelic orange, yellow, cerise – the colours of the spices heaped on streetside stalls. The camera clunked against Nathan's ribs. He closed his eyes, opened them again, focusing on the translucent vest stretched taut across the driver's back. At the hotel, the man hauled his pack inside before Nathan could stop him. He spoke Hindi to the desk clerk.

'He says he tells you 'bout my hotel.'

Nathan made the cash sign with his fingers. 'He's trying it on.'

The clerk and the driver's quarrel pressed like thumbs into Nathan's eye sockets. He craved sleep and warmth and wellness. Two nights. Whatever he was coming down with, he would have to take with him, to Delhi, for the meeting with the German. She was the one who had told him about this hotel. *Indians, mostly. You stay where Westerners stay, it is a risk*. It was a four-storey colonial building fronting on to a plaza kaleidoscopic with traffic. Grime mottled the stone fascia and, over the entrance, the hotel name had weathered from red to pale pink. The lobby smelled of turmeric and something sweetly indecipherable. Nathan looked around for a chair. There wasn't one. As he filled in the register, sweat leaked from his forehead, smudging the ink. The clerk transcribed passport details into a ledger, and there were the usual forms to complete. Silently, Nathan counted to ten and back down again.

'Rooms are thirty rupees and forty rupees. Forty rupees you have personal WC, shower . . . these things.'

'I'll take a forty-rupee room.'

The clerk inspected the ledger, shaking his head: only the cheaper rooms were available. *Sorry*. He returned the passport and shouted. A boy appeared: skinny, ten or twelve years old, wearing a white vest and dhoti and blue plastic flip-flops. More Hindi. The boy detached a key from a panel of hooks on the wall behind the counter and signalled Nathan to give him his pack. It was almost as big as the boy, chafing his calves as he heaved it up one flight of stairs after another. He said his name was Anil.

Nathan spoke through dredged breath. 'No lift?'

'Lift broken.'

The room was on the top floor, at the end of a long balcony. Engine noise, klaxons and a tannoy-blare of music levitated from below like audible heat-haze. There was a time when he'd have paused for a photo, or just to gaze out across the roof-tops.

'American?'

He shook his head. 'English.'

'Where are you coming from?'

'Today? Jaisalmer.'

'You have taking camel ride?'

Nathan removed a trainer and shook it to release a dusting of sand. Anil liked that. He had shouldered the pack against the wall beside a brown door and was jiggling the key into the lock. Nathan asked about the toilets and showers. *Number three level*. The bed was unmade, there was a light bulb set into one wall, a bedside table, a wash-basin crazed with cracks, a wooden chair, and curtains that were drawn closed, dousing the room in an anaemic green glow. The floor was bare concrete.

Nathan pointed to the bed. 'No mosquito net?'

A grin, a wag of the head. Nathan made a whining noise and jerked his fingers. *Acha!* The boy separated the curtains to disclose a mesh screen mended with strips of sticking-plaster. He searched Nathan's face for approval. Then he switched on the ceiling fan, distributing shadows about the walls. The blades ticked loudly and gave off a smell of scorched metal, the erratic down draught making the curtains dance. Nathan pressed a note into the boy's hand and asked him to fetch tea and bottled water.

'My cousin is kissing.'

'No girls.'

'You like boy?'

'No boys.'

As soon as Anil had gone, Nathan stowed the camera beneath the bed, fastened tightly by its strap to the underside of the wire webbing that supported the mattress. Not ideal, but it would do. He was unpacking when the boy returned. The tea tasted excessively sweet, like it always did. There were biscuits in his pack, but he couldn't face them. When had he last eaten? Jaisalmer. A carton of glutinous dhal and rice from a vendor. Soon he would be eating Western food again. Home in a clean, crisp land where his senses no longer flinched from constant intrusion. He imagined himself at Indira Gandhi, within a week, moneybelt so taut with dollar bills it nipped the flesh as he lowered himself into his seat on the plane. Patience, composure, concentration – that way, the days divided into hours and minutes until you could almost feel their passing. He spoke aloud to the empty room: *do not blow this*. Within minutes of finishing his drink, Nathan puked into the basin – no vomit, just a warm splash of tea. He sat on the bed for a long time, shivering, dampening the sheet with his sweat.

The Bucket

In his waking, he was trapped underwater; a rescue party at the surface played searchlight beams across the sea-bed. His eyes bulged. His chest, his head, pounded with the pressure; limbs so laden with waterlogged clothing he couldn't . . . a persistent knocking, a voice. *Hello, English! Hello!* Morning spilled into his room through rents in the curtains. The voice, again. Anil. Nathan swung his legs out of bed and, sitting up too abruptly, had to suppress a sudden surge of sick. The T-shirt and shorts clung to him as though he'd been shrink-wrapped. He hung his head between his knees, then raised it, shoving damp hair back from his forehead. Still, the knocking.

'Please, open.'

'I don't want any *breakfast*.'

Anil gave three sharp raps. 'You' cup, please.'

Nathan swore. He carried the tea cup from the previous afternoon across the room and yanked the door open. Daylight shrouded the boy in a fluorescent corona that rendered his teeth and clothes supernaturally white.

'Problem?'

'No problem.' Nathan blocked the doorway. 'I was sleeping.'

'Breakfast? Paratha, jam, tea, boil egg, shamble egg, dhal, banana. You what?'

'Nothing. No, OK, bananas.' He held up two fingers.

The stool was the loosest so far, like melted chocolate. It took several minutes to accumulate in the depression between the foot-rests. He used the scoop to flush, then on himself, the cold douche hurting like a bruise. Raising himself from squat position, his knees gave and he had to brace himself against the wall. When Nathan returned from the toilets, he found the brown door ajar even though he had locked it. An old woman was sweeping the floor, stooping to reach under the bed with long scything motions. She became flustered, drawing the headscarf of her sari across her mouth.

'No cleaning now.' He gestured towards the door. 'Go away.'

She pressed her palms together as she hurried out. '*Namaste*.'

Nathan checked the camera. It was still in place. On the floor under the bed was a matchstick, the tin-foil plinth and fragmented ash of a spent mosquito-coil, and a dead cockroach big as a thumb, all gathered in a mound of dust. He surprised himself with his revulsion. Weeks back, in a dorm in Varanasi, he'd passed an hour with two Kiwis watching ants dismantle a roach corpse segment by segment and carry it away.

Nathan sipped from the bottle of water. The bananas he left uneaten on the table. He tried to shave, but there was no hot water and even the lowering of his face over the basin made his head ache so much he had to sit down until the pain abated. It made him fearful, what was happening to his body – afraid of the illness, and of the consequences of failing to deliver. When she'd declared his fee, the German had smiled, then ceased to smile. *Don't do this only for reward, Nathan. We prefer you to think also of the . . . penalty? . . . yes, the penalty of neglecting your obligation to others*. He was beginning to appreciate the subtlety of this differential in motivation. A day, another night, another morning; then, taxi–train–taxi–hotel. Delhi. Job done. Once the delivery was made he could be as sick as he liked.

He needed the toilet again. One of the Kiwis reckoned you could time the intervals between shits, as a woman marks contractions during the onset of labour; Nathan forgot the calculation, but it was supposed to help diagnose proximity to death.

He occupied his bed, perspiring, sleeping or not sleeping, coughing, observing the rotations of the ceiling fan, waiting for Anil. Regularly, urgently, he took himself to the third floor. Hours were no longer calibrated by minutes but by these shuffling excursions. The bananas turned brown then black on his bedside table; a plain biscuit was expelled, soon after its consumption, in undigested chunks. If he drank anything more than a sip of water he retched it back up with such vehemence that he couldn't breathe until the spasm ceased. In the evening, Anil came. Nathan made two demands: a doctor, and a transfer to a room with its own WC. An hour later, the boy returned.

'Forty rupee room all full. Telephoning to doctor is tomorrow.'

'No, now. You must telephone him now. Today.'

'Yes, to-day. But he cannot coming before tomorrow. Wery busy man.'

'I am very sick.'

'Yes, sick.' Anil grinned. 'Doctor tomorrow. No problem.'

'I'm going to Delhi tomorrow. I have to leave here by

twelve, so the doctor must come early. First thing in the
morning. D'you understand?'

   Anil wagged his head. 'Doctor tomorrow, no problem.'

   'Here.'

   The boy accepted the money.

Nathan stole a bucket from a storeroom on the third-floor
landing. A metal pail, pitted with rust but intact. He carried it
to his room and part-filled it with water, standing it in the
corner, beneath the open window.

A Representative in Automotive Components

Morning diluted the shadows, exposing the contents of the
pail – the unexpected, unmistakable colour. Nathan lifted the
bucket on to the window-ledge, tilting it towards the wash of
day, and studied the red until it could not be disputed or
reassessed as some trick of the light. Even allowing for the
container, the smell was ferrous: raw liver, menstruation,
nosebleed. He set the bucket back down. He wiped his
palms on his T-shirt. Jesus. OK, OK, what he had to do was
get help because, what was it? It was only six a.m., but he
needed the doctor right away. He inhaled. If he could make it
as far as the landing and shout down the stairwell . . . his
bowels contracted. The bucket supported his weight once
more, its rim etching deeper into welts of raised flesh. Five
minutes, ten. Sweat speckled the floor between his feet.

   In the night, he had dreamed of a policewoman calling at
his parents' house with news of his death: mother, sobbing
on the sofa; father, correcting the WPC's pronunciation of
Jodhpur. He'd smiled in his sleep, storing his father's remark
for the German. Give her a laugh. Make her like him. But
she'd been there, too, drinking tea with his parents, wanting
to know where he was, where *it* was, threatening them; but
they refused to betray him. All the while, Nathan – invisible,
inaudible – was screaming at them to tell her, to *tell her*, to
take her up to his boyhood bedroom, with its Blu-tacked

bands and footballers, and for *fuck's sake* show her the
fucking hiding-place.

The next time, he woke to garish sunlight. There was a power
cut. The fan must have been idle for some time, because
Nathan lay wreathed in moist sheets. Coming to. Watching
the zigzag of flies in the corner of the room. What time was
it? Five past ten. Fuck. He convinced himself Anil had fetched
the doctor and gone away again, unable to obtain a
response. He sat up, then stood, then let himself out, not
bothering to lock the door or even close it. As he edged
along the balcony, he had to shield his eyes against the
reflective glare of the floor, the walls, the windows; making
sure not to look down into the plaza, humming with dust and
traffic, four storeys below.
  Step. Step. Step.
  If he focused on the floor directly in front of his feet,
concentrating, making each step his sole objective, then the
next one and the next, he would reach the lobby eventually.
And when they saw him, the state of him, they would have to
help.
  Step, step.
  Nathan made the mistake of raising his head, trying to
judge the distance to the landing. There was only sky. Blue
smog-hazy sky. And the sky rearranged itself in a rude
swoop, an arc, a blur of bright wide blueness that blacked
into nothing.

A face loomed over him: moustache, small mole on the
bridge of the nose, yellowish filaments in the whites of the
eyes. A brown face.
  'Are you the doctor?'
  The face frowned, amended its angle. 'In actual fact, I am a
representative in automotive components.'
  'Where's Anil?'
  'Excuse me?'
  'The boy. The room attendant.' He tried to sit up, but a

hand eased him back down on to the softness of a pillow.
'He . . .'

'Please, you need to rest,' said the voice of the face.

Nathan's breath came in short rasps, fractured by fits of
coughing. His head throbbed. There was an alteration in him,
in his skin, and it took a moment to identify towelling where
there had been thin, damp cotton. He was wearing a
bathrobe.

'Where are my clothes?'

'There are clean clothes when you are ready.'

An arm indicated a chair where a pair of shorts and a
striped T-shirt Nathan recognized as his own were neatly laid
out. When he asked how they came to be there, the face
explained that he had *taken the liberty* of fetching them from
his room.

'You went into my room?'

'Ah, you see, but you have defecated all over mine.' A
smile. 'So perhaps that makes us even?'

Nathan noticed the room, now. Much like his own as far as
he could see, only bigger, and the curtains were patterned
with flowers. It smelled of aftershave. He shut his eyes,
opening them again at the resumption of the voice.

'You fell outside my door. *Into* my door, in actual fact.'
Another smile. 'I'm afraid your head is bleeding.'

There was a spasm in his gut. This time he would not be
deterred – pushing, pleading; the hands that restrained him
became his support, helping him from the bed and on to his
feet. *Please, just here.* Nathan saw a partition with a doorway
opening on to a toilet and shower stall. The hands were
guiding him. They held him while he squatted, confident arms
hooped under his in a bear-hug redolent of stale tobacco,
spices and hair oil. That astringent scent of aftershave. When
Nathan had finished, he fumbled with the tap, the scoop, the
logistics of cleaning himself; then the hands other than his
own took charge again: sluicing the water, a palm wiping him
with efficient strokes before using a towel – gentler, now – to
rub him dry. Nathan's eyes filled.

'Please, you are sick. There is no reason to be disgusted with yourself.'

The man was still at the bedside. He had changed. Instead of a vest, he wore a white short-sleeved shirt with a collar, a tie and gold-framed glasses. The distinctive red-and-white markings of a pack of Marlboro showed through the fabric of his breast pocket. He was smoking. Nathan watched his host's hands, the manicured nails and tufts of silky black on the back of each finger; hands that had cleaned him.

'By the by, my name is Venkat.'

Nathan said his own name.

'Do you object?' Venkat said. 'At home, I am not permitted to smoke.'

'How long have I been asleep?'

'A few minutes.'

'What time is it?'

The other man inspected his watch. 'Precisely eleven o'clock.'

'Jesus.'

'Don't worry, the doctor is coming. I have made the necessary arrangements.'

'I have a train to catch. To Delhi.'

Venkat shook his head. 'In actual fact, you are not in a suitable condition for travelling from one side of this room to the other. So I think Delhi is a little ambitious.'

Nathan went to lift himself.

'Please, rest. Unfortunately I have business affairs to attend to, but I shall wait with you until the doctor arrives, if that is agreeable.'

'How soon will he be here?'

The man smiled, tilting his head to expel smoke towards the ceiling. 'I take it you are new to India?'

The abortive attempt to leave, the inability even to dress himself without fainting for a second time – with these failures came the fact, so simple in its irreversibility: the train had departed without him. He would not reach Delhi that night, he would not keep his appointment with the German. He would not deliver. That was the finality. Nathan, his face smeared with tears and spit and snot, became a small boy.

Venkat offered him a handkerchief. 'Perhaps, in a few days, you will be well enough to resume your travels.'

Nathan wiped his eyes, nose, mouth, with the flat of his hand. The weeping was spent almost as soon as it had started. He tugged the borrowed bathrobe close about him, his body depleted and insubstantial. If there was strength, it existed elsewhere; he was not the one with the strength now. Even his host – benign, comforting, slender – looked capable of snapping Nathan's limbs one by one, like chicken bones.

'My room, I've left my valuables in there. Money, and that.'

'I have locked it.' He indicated a key on the bedside table; it was resting on the moneybelt, with its familiar sweat stains. 'Do you have a camera, you see, because I was unable to find one amongst your possessions?'

Nathan hesitated. 'No.'

'You don't like to take pictures of your sightseeing?'

'No. Well, yeah, but it got stolen. In Jaisalmer.'

'Ah, Jaisalmer. I have never visited.'

Nathan described the ancient fort's labyrinthine alley-ways, the camel trek, the drought that had littered carrion – cows, goats, dogs – in the villages of the desert margins, and the screech of jet fighters patrolling the border with Pakistan which, one night, was as close to the camp as Jaisalmer itself. He did not talk of the transaction, completed there, in the bleached wastes.

'You should go there some time.'

His host frowned. 'In actual fact, in the more primitive regions of my country the demand is not so great for automotive components.'

No contact, that was the rule. No excuses. The arrangements, once specified, were not variable. *Security will not be compromised*, those were the German's words.

Failure to deliver on time would automatically constitute a failure to deliver at all.

Nathan handed back the snaps of Venkat's family, their names and ages exchanged for details of his own relations back in England. The business card was Nathan's to keep, his host's home address written on the reverse. Venkat zipped it inside the moneybelt.

'There, in your passport, for safekeeping.' He shut the photos in his wallet. 'Before you leave India you might care to visit, and my wife will cook for you?'

Now that he knew of the years Venkat had spent in Birmingham, learning his trade, Nathan could detect the trace of an accent. *Aston Villa*, *Birmingham City*, *West Bromwich Albion*, *Warwickshire County Cricket Club*. On the other man's lips, these intended intimacies only made Nathan's homeland more inaccessible than ever.

He faked tiredness. Then, the feigned sleep became real; when he awoke again it was dusk and the incense of a smouldering mosquito-coil perfumed the air.

'Where's the doctor?'

'The doctor is coming.'

The Arrival of the Doctor

These sleeps were the best: the dreamy, drifting, anaesthetized loops of waking and semi-waking and deep, deep slumber where all pain was imaginary, light as foam and diffused on the breeze of each outward breath. In these hallucinogenic sleeps, the stink of himself, the wetness between, beneath, his legs: none of it mattered. The camera, the delivery: none of it mattered. He saw the German's face on the ceiling, hologrammed, telling him it was all right it was all right it was all right. They could not reach him or hurt him because he was beyond forgiveness, he had transcended forgiveness; if he could only allow himself to pass to the other side of the sleeping he would be safe from them for ever. But

the moustache was real. The mole on the nose, the
gold-framed glasses. The voice. These were the threads that
snagged him.

The sheet was withdrawn gently, the smell lifting from the
bed like rotting meat, stirring him. His words dried in his
throat.

'Let me go.'

Cold water splashed his face, his hair. 'Please, you must
drink.'

'Let me go.'

'Here.' The water was in his mouth now. 'Try to swallow.'

In the hours that may have been night, he had flown in a
plane in the pitch-dark, its drone – the disturbed mantra-hum
of a bee swarm – always on the point of halting, of stalling, of
cutting out and plunging the aircraft down into the spiralling
black. Him, willing this. Willing the engine to stall. But, in the
daylight, with water being spilled into him and words coaxing
him to swallow, the engine noise persisted in the erratic
propeller gyrations of a ceiling fan in a room that wasn't his.

He was awake.

'You must've missed your business appointments.'

Venkat didn't reply.

'I'm sorry.'

'In actual fact, these matters were not so important.'

'Where did you sleep?'

'Here, in the chair.'

'Thank you.'

'There is no necessity to thank me.'

Voices were using Hindi now. He had the embarrassed sense
of having just spoken out loud in his sleep. Any amount of
time might have elapsed since the last period of lucidity, the
last conversation. Was he participating in this one? No. It was
other people, seemingly talking about him. Drowsy as he
was, the words – their urgent, secretive tone – lured his
attention towards the source of the sound. He turned his

head. Venkat was framed in a rectangle of bright light, before the silhouetted figure of a boy. Anil. In the instant before the door closed, Venkat glanced at Nathan.

'What?'

But he was alone, now, with no one to hear him. The watch face was too blurred for him to decipher the time. Three? Four? It didn't seem possible, but this was the afternoon of his second doctorless day in Venkat's room. Something was wrong. The eavesdropped exchange had left a taste, a palpable essence of unease. When he tried to move, Nathan felt himself empty into the towel that had been swaddled about him as an incontinence pad. He closed his eyes.

Where was Venkat? Nathan spoke the man's name, but received no reply beyond the resonance of his own voice on blank walls. He called out. The exertion initiated a sequence of harsh coughs that left him breathless. It would be the doctor. Probably, he'd gone off to find the doctor and bring him here personally. Make sure he came.

'Venkat? Are you there?'

Fuel tanks, radiators and exhaust systems for the motor-vehicle repair and maintenance sector. That was his area of special responsibility. He promised he'd wait with Nathan until the doctor arrived. He promised that.

The mosquitoes were biting: ankles, ears, knuckles – any place where the veins were vulnerable. Venkat must have gone out without lighting a coil. If the coils and the matches were within reach, maybe Nathan could light one himself.

The light had seeped from white to grey to shadow. Nathan had no idea how long he'd been left alone, but the apprehension of waking up unattended was easing now that he understood the reason. Anil had come – when was that? Today, this afternoon – to report some hitch with the doctor, and the delay had been unacceptable to Venkat. He was out there now, in the city somewhere, explaining the urgency of the circumstances.

Hadn't he lit a coil? He thought he had. But there was no smoke, and the feeding went on. He'd watched a TV documentary back home about a traveller in Mongolia or somewhere whose horse was bitten to death by flies.

Soon there would be footsteps on the balcony, voices – *in here, please*; no, Venkat wouldn't use English – but, anyway, Nathan imagined this: the ushering in of the doctor. For a moment, he became quite euphoric. He considered what to say, after the handshakes and introductions. *Doctor, I would be grateful if you could prescribe something to stop me shitting blood in my friend's bed.* He rehearsed the phrase out loud, repeatedly – making himself laugh so long his ribs hurt.

What was Venkat's wife called? S, something. *Sunita.* Sunita, he had to be sure to remember that. What about the children? One boy, two girls. Or was it the other way round? He couldn't, for the life of him, recall their names.

He was thirsty. Where was the water?

That sleep felt like a long one, although the room appeared no darker now than when he'd drifted off. Still no sign of Venkat. His absence was, in a way, a kind of presence. Nathan liked that notion. This room was busy with absent people: Venkat, the German, Anil, the doctor, the men whose task it would be to track him down and levy the penalty for his failure to deliver. If the levying didn't take place here, it would occur somewhere, sometime; in another room in another Indian city. Except, he was here, now. In Jodhpur. Bedridden. He was going nowhere.

'I'm going nowhere, pal.'

The water was on the bedside table, he remembered, next to the moneybelt and the key to his own room. If he turned his head, he could see the upper half of the bottle. The upper

half had no water in it, just moisture pearling the inside of the
clear plastic. He tried to reach out, but his arm was tangled in
the sheet.

Footsteps. They passed by the window and he heard the
unlocking of a door, followed by noises in the neighbouring
room. The turning on of a tap.

The thirst was worse than the mosquitoes.

Nathan manœuvred himself so that he could lever his
shoulders off the bed, lifting his head and propping himself on
his elbows. After a brief rest, he managed to push again with
his heels. He was almost sitting up now, the wooden
headboard hard against his spine and his skull lolling back
into the wall.

Why was Venkat taking so long?

Nathan regulated his breathing, counting each deep
inhalation until the urge to vomit had receded. Now, the
water. He looked at the bottle on the bedside table. The
moneybelt was still there, along with the key; even in
the gloom of imminent nightfall he could make out their
shapes. But there was something else. Black, irregularly
shaped. It might have been a small animal, crouched there or
curled asleep, its long black tail dangling in a loop over the
edge of the table. He allowed his vision to adjust to the failing
light.

The camera.

It was a moment before he was able to free a hand without
slumping sideways off the bed. He pulled the camera on to
his lap, dislodging the bottle and sending it to the floor where
the water inside continued to slop back and forth after the
bottle itself had come to rest. The back of the camera wasn't
properly closed. He opened it. In doing so, he discovered
why the flap hadn't clicked shut: the package had been
removed and then put back carelessly into place. It had been
unsealed; the tape was damaged and parts of the camera's
interior were powdered with spillage. Nathan had some on
his fingers. He wiped it off.

In that moment, he recalled Venkat's expression as he
stood in the doorway.

Looking around the darkening room, Nathan saw that the
clothes rail beyond the foot of the bed was strung with empty
hangers and the small suitcase no longer stood in the corner.
The towelling robe, which had been rinsed and draped to dry
over the back of the chair – that was missing, too. And if he
could make it to the bathroom, he was sure that the wash
bag would have gone from the ledge above the basin.

Nathan set the camera and the package down.

He didn't need to, but he looked anyway – taking the
moneybelt from the table and, with some difficulty, unzipping
the compartment containing his passport. He opened it,
thumbing methodically through the pages for the business
card with Venkat's home address inscribed on the reverse. It
wasn't there.

The room was in darkness. Nathan had eased himself down
on to his back again, eyes closed, listening to the muted
sounds of the night. Somewhere in the hotel, music was
playing on a radio; in the street, way below, people were
shouting above the buzz of traffic. In here, there was only the
tock-tock of the fan. He sifted the gusts of dispersed air for
the tang of aftershave, but the room's pervasive smell was
the smell of himself. His body felt unnaturally light, held in
place on the bed by the burden of the sheet; he pictured
himself, chalk-white in the black. He closed his eyes. Waiting
for dreams. Waiting for sleep. Waiting for the knock on the
door that would announce the arrival of the doctor.

Please ensure you are at the Boarding Gate at least

airJamaica

BOARDING AS ONLY. NOT VALID FOR TICKETING
passengers arriving late.

Half Moon

Half Moon
Golf, Tennis & Beach Club

P.O. Box 80, Montego Bay, Jamaica
Telephone (876) 953-2211
Telefax (876) 953-2731

01C/115   1 20 0

MARKS H

INFORMATION

01C

NAME

Howard Marks

LONDON TO KINGSTON

Prison Leave

MARKS/HOWARD MR
NAME OF PASSENGER

PNR/CARRIER CODE

CARRIER   FLIGHT   CLASS   DATE   TIME

SEAT NR

AIR JAMAICA

PLACE OF ISSUE

ISSUED BY

Brought up in a South Welsh mining village and educated at Balliol College, Oxford, Howard Marks is best known for successfully smuggling massive consignments of marijuana throughout the world. Operating through forty-three aliases, eighty-nine phone lines and twenty-five companies, he maintained contact with organizations as diverse as MI6, the CIA, the IRA and the Mafia. On release from prison, Howard Marks wrote his bestselling autobiography, Mr Nice, and now vigorously campaigns for the legalization of recreational drugs.

Morgan Price and I looked at each other, then at the prison space we were leaving behind, and then again at each other. But this second look was no mere glance. It was more like a search for an understanding of the intense emotions in our guts and minds: the knowledge of a common destiny, a shared future. Prison hadn't made us gay; it wasn't that one. What about the soul-mate stuff? Had I known Morgan in previous lifetimes but only just started looking through his eyes rather than at them? Does freedom hit everyone this way? If so, let's bottle it up and sell it. Would we scam together? We never had, although we'd been busted as one inseparable unit in Cardiff's Emporium. And we'd both been shafted enough by those we'd trusted in our separate so-called petty-criminal professions, those for whom we would have gladly risked our lives, done our bird, not grassed or cheated. Could we ever trust anyone again, ever correctly predict anyone's actions, ever love again?

Morgan and I hadn't dared talk about scamming: too many screws, too many grasses, too many listening walls – far too many nosy cunts. But through those ten thousand and one games of Scrabble, chess and backgammon, we'd learned each other's deviousness, ruthlessness and courage. We'd heard the other's farts and wet dreams, respectfully looked away when tears had to be stifled, never tried to share a bad mood. We'd been far better to each other than are most lovers. I wouldn't have shagged him if he was the last creature on earth, but I know he wouldn't have minded. The eyes had it, but we didn't even possess our mothers' addresses. Our eyes misted over.

Morgan Bevan Bowen (BB) Price was a Jamaican musteefino, fifteen-sixteenths black and one-sixteenth white.

BB maintained that at least some of the white blood had
come from Henry Morgan, former pirate and later governor of
Jamaica. Having survived a cut-throat childhood upbringing
in Kingston, BB was totally uneducated and possessed no
commercially recognizable skills or aptitudes. All this he had
learned to blame on British colonialism, particularly when
dished out by the ruthless Welsh. Several decades ago BB's
family had left him behind in Jamaica, setting out for Britain –
Tiger Bay – for fortune and fun. That was the last BB had
heard of them.

I live in Devon, but my mother tongue is Welsh and I knew
BB's name meant 'born from the sea, the son of Evan and
the son of Owen and the son of Rhys'. That was definitely
over the top, being the son of three fathers. BB had not even
realized his names were Welsh or that Tiger Bay, the first ever
British Jamaican community, was in Cardiff. And he had not
been pleased to be so told on that first night in the city's cold
damp cells, years ago. I enjoyed rubbing some friendly salt
into his wounds.

'What's more, BB, Henry Morgan was Welsh through and
through.'

BB looked sick and shot me a glance loaded with loathing.
But his hatred danced with some inner amusement. 'Ya kiant
say dat, Jarvis. Me tart Henry Morgan im big boutya. You say
im tiefing rass. Welshing like tiefing.' BB smiled. He knew I
was getting riled.

'Look, BB, Welshing is a name made up by the fucking
English so that no one would trust the Welsh. Gave the dogs
a bad name, and they got kicked. Wales was the first English
colony. And it's still one. Jamaica just had a little taste. But
you're right: Henry Morgan was a great scammer. If it wasn't
for him, Jamaica would have no booze, no singers, probably
no dope. You know, BB, it took a Welshman to give you the
three Rs: rum, reefer and reggae.'

'Dat bullshit, mon. Arawak Indian dem hab booze waters
more dan tousand year back. Ganja a fe Ras Tafari. Nobody

kian give music to Jamaica. Jamaica mek dat for all de world, Jarvis.'

'OK, I was lying about the reggae bit, but Shirley Bassey is Welsh. And that Arawak Indian booze isn't a patch on white rum. As for ganja, that was brought to Jamaica by Indians from Bombay. I promise you. That's why it's the same word.'

The ensuing years spawned several such banters, and on this goodbye day they sprang to our minds and attempted to penetrate our misty eyes, trying to comfort us in the certainty of our uncertainty and in the fear of our known destiny. My resolve weakened.

'BB, shall I give you a way of always being able to get hold of me?'

'No, mon. Ya af to leave it to Jah, mon.'

Seeming reality replaced the fear of final farewell and I, Jenkin Jarvis, found myself living with my mother, who ran a small guest-house in Hanging Post Hill, Devon. I wasn't allowed to drink, associate with convicts or travel more than a few miles from home. So I grew some skunk in the garden shed. It was good. I sold some: they always came back for more.

The parole conditions were finally lifted and I could get away from it all: should I put on a rucksack and hitchhike, get a skinhead haircut and fly to Goa, take mind-blowing drugs, wear a disguise and rent a bedsit in Shepherd's Bush or simply sleep? I'd made about £500 from my illegal horticultural activities, so could actually exploit, or at least test, my fantasy of visiting Jamaica and accidentally bumping into BB.

'Jenkin, be careful of the hurricanes, mind,' said my mother as we kissed goodbye at Heathrow's Terminal 3, 'and don't go breaking any more laws.'

Reality sank back.

I hadn't flown for ten years. Flocks of excited butterflies danced in my guts as I stuck a small piece of Moroccan hash further up my rectum: I might not be able to score for a few hours after landing in Jamaica. Conventional wisdom mandates taking no coal to Newcastle, but a Welsh miner's son can only blame himself if he freezes to death for not doing so. My excitement, however, diluted into manifestations of acute withdrawal symptoms when I discovered that Air Jamaica operated a strict no-smoking policy. Then, a bold-typed notice on my airline ticket sprang right into my face: 'You can help: Report drug smuggling to US Customs 1-800-etc.' The cold turkey swiftly gave way to fear and loathing, but there was a comforting inference: at least the Jamaican authorities couldn't be bothered to divulge their telephone number. BB had often explained to me that a few dozen goats were immeasurably more effective and considerably cheaper than US helicopters in tracking down marijuana plantations. But the prospect of ten smokeless hours was really vexing. Resorting to the old trick of fitting a condom over the toilet's smoke alarm, I smoked a joint, sat down back at my seat, read some guides to Jamaica and took some Valium.

I woke up to a clear view of Jamaica, some tropical fruit juice and a small refreshing towel. Before hitting the battered Montego Bay airport runway, a quick glimpse of the nearest hotel, the Buccaneer, reawakened the tranquillized stomach butterflies.

A spell of years off the streets had resulted in my having a clean licence, a virgin passport and a valid credit card, so I proudly presented my documents to the car-hire desk. Within a few minutes I was behind the wheel in the car park. An hour later I was still there, but a great deal more stoned. Where should I drive?

The guidebooks I'd read on the plane were luring punters to chill out in genuine plantation houses or plastic Disneyland castles; drunkenly tear around Georgian urbanizations in golf carts; bed-and-breakfast in celebrity traps, rain forests or enchanted gardens; or enjoy traditional pursuits like honeymooning, conferring, reuniting with family members and taking medically prescribed Viagra with fellow geriatrics. Not for me. But the worst on offer was the All Inclusive (or American) Plan, which threw in everything American tourists want: American food, American satellite television, water sports, night-lit tennis courts and world-class golf courses – where they can sit red-faced in linen suits, think vaguely racist thoughts and be served rum punches by white-gloved waiters. Fuck that.

Then I read about the manatees: Columbus spotted them in 1494 and identified them as mermaids. They were beautiful, strictly vegetarian and doted on each other and their young. A significant percentage of their population lived in Jamaica. The only downside was that now, manatees were 14 foot long, ate 400 kilos of sea grass every day, were ugly as fuck, and were known as sea cows. What went wrong, Darwin? Jamaican manatees live in Alligator Hole, in the middle of the south coast of the island. I took out my free map, found Alligator Hole and decided to drive straight down to the coast road, turn left, stop at Belmont, birthplace and burial place of Peter Tosh – 'Legalize It' – pay my respects, then cruise through the excitingly named Black River, the main town of Saint Elisabeth, Morgan Bevan Bowen Price's old stomping ground. That'll work.

I eased out into the jumping traffic of Jamaica, the country with the greatest number of road deaths per capita in the world (excepting India and Ethiopia, which also have more dope and Rastas). Jamaica certainly has its fatal side: the obeahman with his voodoo curses, malevolent duppies (small ghosts that live in trees), the Undertaker's Wind, the Doctor's Wind, John Crow the carrion vulture. Soon com. They came to Ian Fleming and Noël Coward. Bad place to write.

From Black River, I headed to Treasure Beach, a well-known ganja-smoking community. Morgan BB Price had fondly referred to Nannyland, so I took a sign bearing its name. It led to a sprawling unattended seaside site with statues and monuments dedicated to black heroes. Nanny, known also as Queen Nanny or the Right Excellent Nanny led the Maroons (descendants of Spanish-owned slaves freed by the Spaniards to harass the invading British). Never harmed, never armed, Nanny is the only Jamaican heroine and the subject of countless Jamaican songs and legends. While her head was in the bush, she could catch bullets with her arse and deliver them straight back into the hearts of the enemy. Close by, without the aid of flame or heat, Nanny kept a cauldron of boiling water ready for Welshmen. Leek soup. Time for another joint.

I drove by a very closed wooden shack named the International Communication Centre. As a result of either sharp business practice or rural rage, all phone boxes within striking distance had been vandalized. I kept walking, passing bars and other flimsy attractions which had come about as excuses to design, commission and erect signs. Bars may go bust in weeks, but the signs live on for years. I came to Jimmy's Sea Food. The outside was plastered with notices proclaiming: 'Conch puts you in high gear'; 'You get blood from lobsters'; 'God is the highest'; 'When the Devil Says No, God Says Yes'; and 'Live by the clock, die by the clock'. It was closed.

Nearby, I noticed large parcels of land clearly owned by middle-class people who lived miles away. Clearly no one with any money stayed here any longer than they had to; consequently, the land was worthless and yielded nothing but problems, certainly no rent. It was the difficulty of getting rid of the land alone that made the owners keep it and feel obliged to spend annual vacations evicting squatters and destroying signs.

A bar called Sue's Little Pleasure had just opened its door. I walked into a shed 12 foot square, with bamboo walls, pitched zinc roof, concrete floor, solid wooden bar, one framed photograph of Haile Selassie, and several unframed photographs and paintings of Saint Bob Marley. A few awkward stools of different heights stood at the bar; another lay on the floor. Several pairs of ladies' shoes lay for sale on the bar, which also carried a deafening ghetto blaster, badly tuned in to a local radio station. Behind the bar were two crates of Red Stripe and a shelf of rum bottles. On another shelf were dozens of small, identical bottles of nail varnish. Also behind the bar was the incredibly sexy Dorothy. White men like thin Jamaican girls; Jamaican men like good-sized women with enormous posteriors; white women like dreads, held in contempt by most self-respecting Jamaican girls; everyone is happy. Dorothy gave me a Red Stripe, giggled and disappeared. I took the can to a seat outside. A Rasta joined me. We idly watched seven dogs trying to penetrate a bitch and smiled knowingly at her indiscretion. We knew they were all like that really.

From the teachings of a radical black activist called Marcus Garvey, Rastafarianism grew up in the Kingston slums to become the spiritual nationality of Jamaica and the island's most compelling cultural force. Garvey believed that former slaves must be repatriated back to Africa to establish their own nation state. Garvey prophesied that a black king would arise to lead them. In 1930 tribal warlord Lij Tafari Makonnen (Ras Tafari) was crowned Emperor of Ethiopia. His ancestry could be traced back to Menelik, the product of the sexual union of Solomon (King of Israel) and Makeda (Queen of Sheba). Haile Selassie was acclaimed in Kingston as a living god. God is black.

Rastas are the lost tribes of Israel, sold by Nebuchadnezzar into slavery in Babylon and awaiting their return to Zion, the Promised Land (as in the Boney M song). Rastas grow their hair into dreadlocks, for no razor shall touch the heads of the righteous. Rastas don't eat meat or shellfish; they eat I-tal food: grains, fruit, roots and vegetables. Ganja is the sacramental herb: the healing of the nations. Ganja provides the line of communication with God who exists in each person.

Come to think of it, Rasta must be the ideal religion for the twenty-first century: no written rules, no formal structure, its own drug, its own haircut (which Whitey is jealous of), and a magnetic and charismatic messiah.

Dreads are of three types:

(1) the Wholly Dread, whose diet is strictly salt-free, pork-free, fungus-free, nasty-chemical-free; who sings incantations to Jah while smoking ganja religiously; and who generally leads a peaceful, harmless and meditative life. Wholly Dreads will not sell ganja to Whitey and tend to speak their own largely incomprehensible language.

(2) the Wicked or Cool Dread, who has deep respect for all the above principles, particularly ganja-smoking, but likes Red Stripe, magic mushrooms, headbanging reggae and jerk pork far too much to observe all of them. The Cool Dread will happily sell a good deal of ganja to anyone who appears cool.

(3) the Rental Dread, to whom Rasta is a hairstyle which white wuman dem found sexy. Rental Dreads eat, smoke, sell and sniff anything; they seduce overweight white spinsters and divorcees for the mutually desired goal of sex and sport, financed by the seducee. Rental Dreads try hard not to learn English: it diminishes their mystery and exposes them to difficult and searching questions about their religion and lifestyle.

Luckily, my new companion was a Cool Dread. I procured a modest ganja supply, smoked some and let my ears do some work.

BB had been right about Jamaican music: it was hard to discern any dominant Welsh influence. On parole, I'd studied a bit of the island's musical history: Trinidad calypso had combined South American tango and samba to produce the purely Jamaican mento. American R&B and swing combined with mento to produce ska (or bluebeat) i.e. Millie and her sucking lollipops. Ska slowed down to yield rocksteady, 'You Can Get It If You Really Want It'. Then came reggae, derived from Rex, the music of the lion kings of Judah, the music of the town of kings, Kingston. *Jah-Ras Tafari. Jah-maica.* Reggae fused with popular American music to give hip-hop, fused with British popular music to form jungle and fused with the rest of Jamaican music to form dancehall, currently blasting from the one-roomed ghetto of Sue's Little Pleasure.

Abruptly, the radio stopped playing and was replaced by a haunting silence. Everyone was quiet while the radio proceeded to solemnly issue a warning from the Office of Disaster Preparedness & Emergency Management: a Category 4/5 hurricane called Mitch was about to hit Jamaica. The beautiful Dorothy reappeared with panic in her eyes. Cool Dread spoke up: 'Everytime dey say horrican com on de radio, it always turn back. Ya kiant believe dat man pon de radio. Nobody know where a horrican can go. Only Jah know dat, mon.'

The bar's clientele, however, believed the radio man and hastily began washing away tropical-storm phobia with gallons of white rum referred to as 'front-end loaders'. Sugar cane beats hurricane. I got slaughtered as the gentle breeze grew into a gale. Suddenly, the wind quadrupled in ferocity, windows shattered randomly, large objects flew by and the tops of the palm trees all simultaneously faced the same direction, turning into Red Indian chiefs' full-feathered headwear. The sea took a deep breath, moved from the horizontal to the vertical plane and splashed on top of us. The wind and water died down, but we were warned by the Office of Disaster Preparedness & Emergency Management that the relative calm would not last long.

People began flocking to the fishing-boat station to see if they could be useful. The streets had become canals filled with mud, pulped vegetation and grotesquely unfamiliar denizens of the deep. I spotted Dorothy in the middle of the road. She was tormenting a giant crab by sticking her bare toes in its mouth and quickly withdrawing them while the disoriented crab pathetically clapped its clumsy claws. I sidled up to her and asked, 'Would you like to come for a drive in my car before it gets windy again?'

'No,' replied Dorothy, 'me af to be ome in case de roof blow off. Mitch soon com agen.'

'So can I at least walk you home?' I asked.

Her eyes answered, and all I could see was her smile.

'Dat awrite. Just pray to de Lawd dat me bredda not ome.'

The house was empty. Dorothy changed from her brine-soaked rags into a dick-hardening bright-red miniskirt. I could see her white knickers as she sat down to roll a spliff. I felt like a schoolboy seeking the sanctuary of a wank, not wanting to risk her rejection, not wanting to risk her breath smelling badly, or her skin feeling cold, not wanting to think it was all in my head.

The Stray Cats' 'Too Greedy' fought against the wind and was winning, easily. The optimistic anticipation of imminent carnal pleasure made me sneeze.

'Bless you, Jenkin. An agen. An agen.'

Dorothy held out her hand. God! It was for real. We really were going to fuck the fuck out of each other. But I was getting too turned on by the present anticipation. Keep it going, because once I pick the fruit, cherry or not, it will wither. And I might come too quickly. Dorothy stood up and started undoing her buttons.

'Not yet, Dorothy, please. Let's go out and look at the storm. I love it.'

I gently turned the door knob; the weather did the rest. Everything howled as outside replaced inside. Framed in the door was a handsome Rasta. He was holding an Uzi and aiming it at my head.

'Sister, ya kiant do a rudeness like dis.'

'No, BB, no. A fe me fren. Im big boutya fram London. Im luv Jah. No. BB, no. Ya kiant.'

The light suddenly blinded me. I was on the top bunk and the bulb was really close to my eyes.

'Sorry, BB, but this stuff is playing hell with my guts. I have to shit in the bucket.'

'Slop out soon com, Jarvis. Wait, mon. Respect.'

'Yeah, OK. How was your trip, BB?'

'Strange, mon. I on Death Row, mon, and you de 'angman about to kill me.'

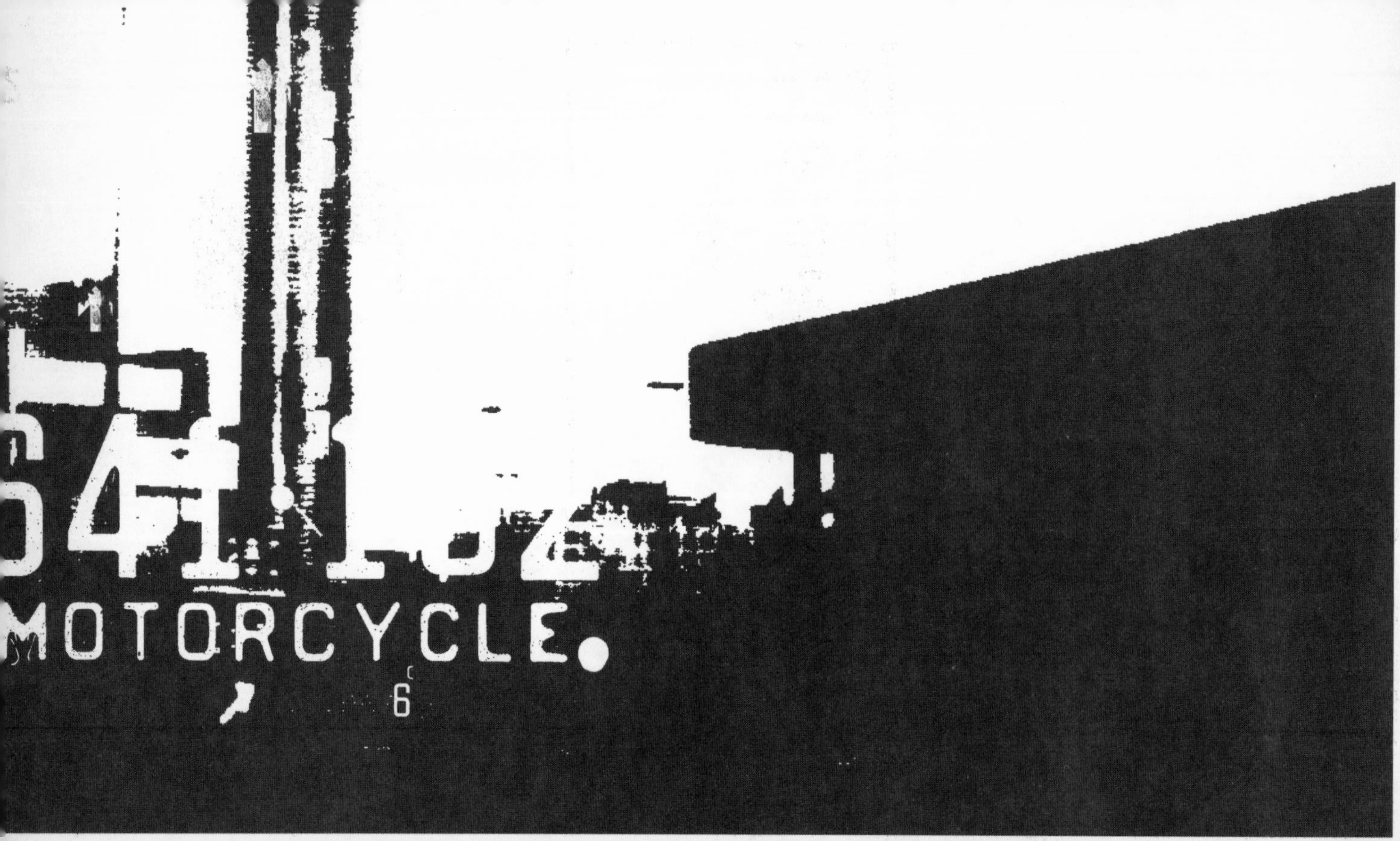
MOTORCYCLE.

Helena Mulkerns

Shiprock

Helena Mulkerns is a Dublin-born writer and freelance journalist whose work has appeared in Hot Press, Rolling Stone, The Irish Times, The Irish in America (Hyperion Books), Film Ireland, IT Magazine and Cineaste, among many others. Her short fiction has been broadly anthologized and nominated for the Sunday/Hennessy Cognac Literary awards and the American Pushcart Prize. She is a founder member of BANSHEE (www.banshee.cnchost.com), lives in Guatemala and has a particular fondness for computers, platform shoes, good tequila and motorbikes.

No smiles. No phone. No spark-plugs. He peered out over the dusty compound at the sandy-purple mountains in the distance, nursing a weak coffee in his hand. He felt lonely. This kind of melancholy came over him from time to time, but was often quite sweet, savourable. Usually you could break it at any point by stopping in some place, getting into a conversation with barmen, truckers, garage attendants, playing a jukebox or a game of pool – and it usually worked. The last two days had been different, though.

The news nagged at him on and off as he travelled, like flimsy remnants of nightmare sneaking momentarily into the waking hours of the dreamer. Occasionally it struck at him from the inside, like a tiny explosion within the space under his ribs, unbearable for a moment and then dissipating with no after-effects. Mostly he just didn't feel as if it was real at all. Maybe it was the sunshine or the isolation of the open spaces that anaesthetized him. The addictive spell of the highway's white lines, no sound other than the bike's song.

He'd ridden south from Colorado, through aspen-clad mountains to Coyote, on roads so gusty they teased the bike into a scary, curvaceous dance. Then the slopes fell away into aridity as he came down into Navajo Nation.

He'd run out of change back at Lagunitas, and he knew that he should have called his sister back there, but hadn't, and now apparently there was no phone. What did he need to know, anyway? There was only one thing to know and the details hardly mattered. It echoed in his head now briefly, the hollow clanking sound of the coins disappearing down the machine, Aileen's voice sounding unfamiliar over the bad connection, forgetting to tell him until the very end of the call, when it all came tumbling down the line in a panic.

– Sorry, Bren, I meant to tell you before . . . shit, it's been two months, you see . . . they brought her back from Greece. Sorry . . . sorry . . .

. . . *Please deposit three dollars for the next minute* . . .

Click, buzz.

The only sound then was a squawky bird cutting across the cloudless desert sky.

He felt dried up, untouched by it. Or rather, he didn't know how he felt. To take his mind off the whole thing, in these past two days he'd been overtaken by a troubled unease that had nothing to do with Tara, or anything really. The stony faces he had encountered since crossing the border into Navajo Nation – they bothered him. It wasn't that they were openly hostile mostly, but it was just that the bullshit was gone. All along the way it had been *Have a nice day. Sir.* Billboards that undermined the intelligence, fast food that threatened the intestines. An easy veneer of blinding friendliness and clean, efficient service with a smile. Maybe he just needed some of that at the moment.

He had a sense of karmic justice – why the hell should the Navajo smile at him? Not that he'd personally been involved, like, but you couldn't look straight into the jet-black eyes and not get the message. It was a subtle understanding carefully folded in with their silence. He felt somehow as if the sky-blessed spires of rock that towered over the motorbike as he threaded his way west spoke for the sullen faces. Betrayal, they thundered. Theft, slaughter, betrayal. Greed, rape, genocide, betrayal.

The Taos he'd got wasted with two heads in a bar where the Sheriff had caught him in the toilet and warned him not to get the locals drunk. He'd told the badge to fuck off. Edward and Tom and himself all ended up on an adobe roof in the old pueblo later, freezing their asses off under the stars and swapping stories about the Spanish and the English, Cortez and Cromwell. The Transcendental Post-Colonial Whinge: *both our people suffered, guys – robbery, persecution and exploitation.*

There'd been fraternal commiserations and large-scale speculation about cultural identity and ethnic pride. They'd all had a great, moon-howling time. But try and pull that one on the Navajo, he thought, and they'd probably tell you how many of Custer's outfits were Irish, or ask you where Eddie Murphy got his name.

He finished the coffee and bundled everything up under the bungee cords – the spark-plugs could wait until this evening. The autumn air was crisp and clear and the russet crags contrasted brilliantly against the turquoise as he looked up. Greece. What the fuck had she been doing in Greece? Aileen hadn't had time to say how it happened, and anyway, he had a fair idea. Tara could always hitch a ride with any amount of her charms: the Bambi eyes, the laugh. They were always the first thing to cause trouble, too.

He remembered them once being unstudied, spontaneous, the legs gangly, the eyes crudely daubed with black the first Christmas her mother ever let her out to midnight mass. She'd caused an uproar in the church that night, after the priest said 'Lamb of God', when she emitted a loud 'mbaaa'. Funny-Tara. Brazen, voracious, life-owes-me Tara.

They'd gone to Greece once, the summer in between his first and second year. That was after the dreaded Hamburg stint . . . slave-labour in the rubber factory, sleeping in what Sean Arnston called *The Sheds* – Ah man, it was *the sheds* – . Working beside sad Turkish men condemned for life, while all he could think of was Tara, and getting out of The Sheds with enough cash to take her to a Mediterranean island. He did. She told him he smelled like a condom. She pampered him and spent his money for three days, then pulled the most outrageous traveller's cheque scam without warning, nearly giving him a heart attack.

After a couple of hours back on the bike, the most bizarre thing began to happen. Gradually, as he drove on towards Shiprock, the road became more and more jammed with cars. He was eventually surrounded by vehicles pushing and chugging, music blaring, with kids and dogs in the back and

mammas and daddies in the front seats. On both sides of the
road, broad expanses of open wilderness yawned at the sky
while he found himself forced to chug along the outskirts of
the rush, which already formed two crowded lanes on the
narrow road. Bren squinted at the glittering coil of vehicles
winding all the way ahead like a drunken rattlesnake.

He was in major trouble now, as the blazing afternoon
temperature forced the engine to overheat. The stop/start
nature of his progress was made worse by the fouled sparks,
the fuel mix having been affected by the high altitude in the
mountains. He was a fool to have forgotten spare plugs. He'd
stop and let it cool off in Shiprock. But what the hell was all
the traffic doing, in the middle of nowhere? He pulled in
beside a red pick-up with a bunch of young lads inside, in
flying form.

– What's the story, fellas? Party, huh?

– It's the fair, man. Have a beer . . .

He was kind of blown away by this, considering the local
laws on alk – but needed no further persuasion, pulling off his
helmet and snapping open the can.

Shiprock – a mutant galleon frozen to stone in a sandy
ocean – erupted like a commandment out of the plain in the
distance. By the time the convoy got into the town itself it
was getting dark. He'd had a fair few beers out of the Indian
lads' cooler by now, but he unfortunately lost the pick-up as it
turned off into a temporary car park along the way. On his left
as he came into the town a large float was crowded with a
born-again-Christian Native American rap group,
chicka-boom-booming on about Jesus saving, with some
token Indian drums overwhelmed by a hollow synth beat.

He parked the bike across the street from the fair
enclosure, with its huge black-and-white banner draped over
the entrance: '65th Navajo Nation Fair'. The cacophony of
sounds hit him in haphazard chorus as he cut the engine,
and he smiled in amazement as he heard the loudspeakers
describe the rodeo inside, the floodlights of the stadium
illuminating the sky. Rockets shot up in the air intermittently

the kids ran around sporting sparklers and Day-Glo necklaces. Madonna blared from one end of the grounds and from the other a fairground organ.

Inside, he wandered about taking in rush after rush of visual onslaught: horses, steer, dogs, carousels, rides, rifle ranges. Pyramids of people clambering up on the fences around the central enclosure to see the young guys belting out into the ring to challenge death in a primal test of worth. Some were winning, some were being carted off in the ambulances that hovered on the south side of the arena. Small faces full of wonder, older kids hopping on rides and consuming dubious looking hot dogs and sweetmeats. Ancient, gnarled characters with skin like the old fishermen in Connemara, the same eyes squinting out at the night with the triumph of seventy-odd years in the wind and sun and rock behind them.

He was chatting away to people now, making the rounds of the stands. At one point he spotted a wide-brimmed hat with a splendid turquoise-and-silver band, and his first thought was to buy it immediately for Tara. His second thought was that he couldn't buy it for Tara, because Tara was dead. Again, the brief, terrifying explosion. She'd always loved hats. He bought it anyway.

– *And Brendan wears a jacket from Toner's Leathers, and a jaunty felt hat to complete his Marlboro Man ensemble . . .*

Nearby, two little guys were waiting to go on a ride. At the entrance, there was a bar four feet from the ground with a sign reading, 'If you don't reach this line, you don't ride!' The bar was way over one little fella's head, and he was raising blue bloody murder. The kids' granny was falling around laughing, and she voiced a loud comment that set everybody in the crowd off, including the child, delighted at the attention. Bren grinned like an idiot. The old lady had spoken in a language he'd never heard before. Looking around carefully, he realized he was the only non-Native American in the entire place.

And I'm five thousand miles from my home he sang to

himself, visualizing the overhead shot: a slow zoom in on
the Gael as he cops that this is a private party. Wide shot:
man in unlikely hat crosses the fairground, concluding he
must continue along his lonely way, on his faithful steed,
Kawasaki.

As he passed by a rifle range, Bren's head and shoulders
unexpectedly came into contact at substantial velocity with a
large wooden sign which had been leaning against a fence.
Topple, crash. Bollix. Momentary blurred focus – *Thank God
he'd just bought the jayzis hat.* There was a small commotion
as four or five kids lifted the board up off him. The rifle-range
guy was out like a flash, and then there he was, being fussed
over by a crowd of fascinated faces, illuminated purple and
green in the flashing lights of a carousel. He felt a large bump
forming on his left temple, but luckily, he wasn't badly hurt.
Now he really felt like a spare prick at a whore's wedding.

The rifle-range guy, a wired-up kid with a long ponytail and
a Guns 'n' Roses T-shirt, shooed everybody away and
brought Bren into what appeared to be a small office trailer.
An elderly woman handed a homemade ice pack through the
door, and Bren put it to his head. He was OK, but the lonely
thing had hit him again, worse this time in the confusion of
the blow. The fairground sounds began to fall away from him
scarily, the voices around him diminished into the distance,
and it was a minute before he could discern exactly what was
up.

Outside, playing out all over the fairground, through the
loudspeakers – the one dance song that could make him
break down . . .

Bloody song. God, he hadn't heard it for years. It welled
out into the garbled night, engulfing him like a gas,
overcoming him before he had a chance, bursting open
some kind of memory bank full of images and smells and
fears way too far back. He tried to concentrate on what the
rifle-range guy was saying, but the song won over.

The sweetness of the lead crept up slowly over the bass,
and the emotive vocals whispered awhile before soaring

somehow, out through his own choked throat, mysteriously
forcing his eyes to blister and his fists to clench.

They played it all the time that summer. She was supposed
to be off getting sorted out, except that she didn't. Instead,
she alighted the plane from Amsterdam in a state of
semi-catatonia, five and a half stone and completely mute.
Nobody ever found out exactly what happened.

– Man! You OK, fella?

The rifle guy was quite taken aback at the sight of this big
motorcycle dude crumbling like a child in the middle of his
office.

– Are you really hurt?

– Ah, shit, look, I'm sorry . . . somebody died is all . . .

– Aw, shit, OK, hang on. I'll be back in a minute.

Jesus. Every house on the road was coming back to him.
Every tree he passed every evening, crossing the dual
carriageway *en route* to the hospital, Walkman-smothered
ears, heart in stasis. The sheer anguish of that dreaded walk,
the hesitation in front of the modern, smoked-glass doors of
the place. White-uniformed penguins, skin-coloured nylons
on them and smelling of Dettol. The gaunt, absent people
wandering by, barely camouflaging their hauntings under
pale-pink fluffy dressing-gowns or Dunnes Stores men's
bathrobes, new for the occasion and ill-worn.

God, that song. It stayed at the top for weeks, and every
damn station played it endlessly. It wasn't even a love song, it
was a song of obsession, of torment, of betrayal. The singer
wound up into such a state of despair it wasn't funny, and yet
every young one went around the estate singing it like an
anthem. And in the end, it got him as well. He had forgotten
this song.

Tara: helpless-Tara, half there, half submerged somewhere
deep in whatever her own haunting happened to be – one he
never really understood. Pale, quivering claws fumbling with
the twenty Major, gentle-Tara whispers that commenced
cryptic sentences only to cut short half-way, darting her eyes
wildly off into the air, as if the culminating words had escaped

out of her on the exhaled smoke. Him trying to hold back,
nodding and smiling like the stupid fuck he was.

He had forgotten how the song drowned his helplessness
in its pathos, how the echoing strings soothed his
bewilderment, how the guitar tapestry somehow rounded out
her skeletal features, the vocal tremor strengthened her
voice, the bass line softened the shoulderblades that nearly
cut a hole through his palm as he kissed her goodbye each
evening.

Without warning, the kid came thumping back into the
trailer and slipped a partially full naggin of Wild Turkey under
his hand, conspiratorially. 'Don't let anyone see that, OK? I
gotta get back out to the stand . . .' He breezed off again, this
time closing the door behind him, easing the last bars of the
song out of his head into the compound outside.

– Please don't go, Bren, she had begged him.

– I'm just really afraid. They've taken everything out of my
head, and I kind of think, like, there's nothing left . . . He
couldn't leave her now, please. She was going to get sorted
out, she'd be grand soon. This time it would work out,
promise.

Another promise to break. Another time to wait. Bren had
given everything away down the years that he'd had to give:
bailed her out, set her up, loved her, brothered her, been
cheated by her, lied to and betrayed. At some point he'd
persuaded himself she was a masochistic figment of his
sexual imagination, and he was sticking to that. This time she
was in the kind of state where he couldn't help her. He
wasn't going to help her.

He'd picked up his bag at reception and stalked straight
outside to get the bus, down to the boat, thinking of her as it
pulled away from the quay. How many times had he thought
of her since then, *please don't go*.

She'd been grand before long, you see, that was the
problem. Then he was sorry. Two Christmases later he ran
into her perched on a stool in *The Palace* with some film guy
from London. She had her mini pulled up around her thighs

like a schoolgirl and she was sniggering at him. Her bitterness, hiding within each sweet nod, each cutesy move on the stool, each flick of the aubergine hair, lashed out at him furiously between the smiles and the slags. So she was back in form, apparently. She was grand, and there was only one minor problem: the look lurking deep underneath the lashes that she couldn't manage to hide from him that said simply: *I can't take too much more of this*.

The song echoed from the back of Bren's brain in continual replay. The Fender distortion, the orchestral touches, the drum folding in half-way like a coked-up heartbeat. The way the singer's repeated phrases hurtled the whole thing into total release before winding down into a ghostly duet of guitar and percussion, into silence. It was a dark-blue song, it was a terrible song. Funny, as he thought it over, it never said what happened in the end.

In the end, what had he expected anyway? That was probably it. He'd only *expected*. That one of these Christmases he'd go home and she'd be there, sorted out. Grand. He'd expected the usual reunion, only this time she'd be ready to do it for keeps. He'd expected one Christmas he'd have something put by, there'd be a decent job somewhere . . . he'd expected too fuckan much.

He drained the bottle. The battered heater in the corner crackled as a piece of chipboard fell from the ceiling and fried on one of the hot orange bars. *Christ, had that really been too much ever to ask for?* He couldn't figure out what was so difficult about it, didn't other people do it? Maybe not Tara. Maybe not him.

As he opened the door, a wave of ecstatic sound and brilliant flashing lights attacked him. He nodded his thanks to the rifle-range guy as he headed back to the bike. The nearest town he could see on the map that looked like it might have a motel was about forty miles off, twenty out of his way. Maybe there'd be something at that crossroads. Or maybe he could camp.

Pulling out of the town, he leaned over and accelerated,

taking a curve in a far too exaggerated fashion, skidding on the gravel and provoking some hoots of encouragement from a gang of kids at the edge of the car park. Sweeping back up to vertical again on the straight of the road, by the time his heart had stopped pounding he was surrounded by cold darkness and out of range of the fairground commotion.

So Tara had been flown home in a box, right. *Dead-Tara*: it seemed as surreal and savage as the ancient bleakness around him. The fair had tumbled up his brain into a mash, and he was still quite drunk as he spotted the gas station at Teec Nos Pos, materializing like a UFO on the crossroads in the distance. Fuck weak coffee, he thought. And camping. And spark-plugs. If he just kept driving, he could make Monument Valley for the dawn.

The night was black as hell, now – without song. It was fuckan creepy, but he kind of wallowed in it. He accelerated to spite the cold, and he kept accelerating to spite himself, ignoring the neon needle as it pushed around the blurred speedometer. The moving patch of ground illuminated in the headlight hurtled crazily towards him; everything was soaring, only the remote sky was still. In the onslaught of the elements, he began to imagine himself losing touch with the bike. The air was lifting him, rocketing all around his body until he was flying on a high-speed, airborne limbo, until he was a nothing, a mere speck in the vastness, merging gradually with the engine's mantra-howl.

To be kept until arrival.
Do not change seat without consulting
your cabin attendant.

C 60190

1 016 2120 87520

IT NUMBER AND

Esther Freud

Such a Nice Time

Esther Freud was born in London but, aged four, moved to Morocco, where she spent two years travelling with her mother and sister. This formative experience gave her the inspiration for her first novel Hideous Kinky, which has now been made into a film starring Kate Winslet. Her second novel Peerless Flats is set resolutely in London. Gaglow, her third, gave her the opportunity to drive around East Germany for her research.

It took five hours to get across the island, from the airport to the sea. 'There she is.' Anna pressed her face against the window of the bus, and as Paul craned to see, Pip looked up and they both saw that she'd been crying.

'What's wrong?' Anna ran over to her. 'What is it?'

'It's Eduardo. He's . . . he's . . . we've argued.' Pip was trembling. 'You know, I'd like to stab him with a knife.'

Anna paled. 'Argued? About what?' She and Paul never argued. She couldn't imagine how they'd start. 'Would it be better if we looked for a hotel?'

'No!' Pip wiped her eyes. 'I've been longing to see you.' She sniffed and laughed. 'Anyway, it will do Eduardo good to see that some couples can be perfectly civilized. And still be happy . . .'

Paul put his arm around Anna and insisted on carrying her bag.

'He's gorgeous,' Pip whispered as they walked towards the boat.

For almost a year Pip and Eduardo had been living in Corsica on a forty-foot aluminium yacht that belonged to an uncle of Eduardo's. Inside everything was made of wood and attached by bolts to the floor or walls. The plates and cups were unbreakable, the glasses bounced and even the washing-up liquid had a designed fixture to keep it in its place.

Anna and Paul were given a cabin to the left of the stern. It was a low-ceilinged cubby-hole with a double mattress covering the floor. Pip and Eduardo whispered furiously on the other side of the wall. Poor Pip, Anna thought, and she cuddled fondly in against Paul's back.

When Anna woke, Paul was already up. She could hear

him chatting brightly in the living area. Anna lay still for a
while, listening to the sea water washing up against the hull in
little bursts. A week to go, she thought, six more nights, and
surprised at the despondency of her thoughts, she pulled on
some clothes and stumbled out of the cabin.

'Hello, my love.' Paul put an arm around her. He drew her
close to him on the breakfast bench. She smiled and kissed
the side of his face.

Pip looked as if she had only just stopped crying. She had
a soft look like a damp flower. 'Morning,' she said.

There were fresh croissants on the table and a pot of
strawberry jam. Pip made more tea.

'How is it all going, the business?' Anna asked. There
hadn't been much time to talk the night before, as Eduardo
had an early booking. A group of eight Japanese ladies who
had never dived before.

'The business is going fine.' Pip rolled her eyes.

Anna stood beside her at the sink. 'Why don't you have a
break, spend the day with us?'

'No, I couldn't. It's your holiday. I know how little time you
get together as it is.'

'We'd love it,' Paul insisted. Anna nodded her head
vigorously. 'We really would.'

Pip smiled and looked at them both. 'Really, I'm fine.
Eduardo and me, we're always arguing like this, and then we
make up.' Colour transfused her face. 'Let's just say it's all
worth it.'

Anna looked over at Paul. He was smiling and laughing as
if he knew just what she meant.

It was already hot when Paul and Anna stepped gingerly
along the gangplank and on to the wooden jetty. As they
approached the row of shops that faced the port Anna tried
to remember her school French. '*Fermez-vous la fenêtre*' was
all she could come up with, which was unlikely to come in
useful, especially as they intended buying provisions for a
picnic. They managed to choose, by intricate methods of

pointing and elimination, some bread and cheese and six slices of salami. Paul picked out two bottles of red wine.

'Do we really need two?' Anna asked, and immediately regretted it. 'I mean, won't they be rather heavy?'

Pip had told them to walk along the coast, away from the town, where they'd find a secret beach, perfect for swimming when the tide was out.

'It's too hot,' Paul said, politely unclasping Anna's hand.

He's right, she thought, it is too hot, and they walked on in silence. It was the last week in May and the fields were full of poppies, and bright yellow columbines like Christmas stars. They came across a dead snake lying on a wall. Paul took a photo of it. He prodded it with a stick, and convinced it really was dead, took three more. 'Paul,' Anna said. 'What are you doing?' She wanted to add that film was expensive, and even one photo of a dead snake was likely to be boring when you got it home to Clapham. Paul put the camera back in his bag and strode on.

'Paul.' She hurried after him. 'Is something wrong?'

'No.' He stopped. 'Please.' He held up one hand. 'We're on holiday.'

Yes, Anna thought, yes, we're on holiday.

The beach was a small high stretch of sand under a bare red cliff. The tide was out and there was no one about. Anna spread their towels side by side. 'You coming in for a swim?' She started to pull off her clothes.

'Not yet.' Paul slunk down on to his towel. He looked up at her, and she felt self-consciously aware of her pale, wintery body. She had her bikini on under her clothes and she ran down to the water's edge. She imagined his eyes following her, and she upped her exclamations of pleasure. 'The water is gorgeous,' she yelled, wading in. The water was in fact freezing, but he could find that out for himself. She ducked and rolled and floated on the waves and when she was lulled and warm she wished more than ever that he'd come in and join her. She would clasp him around the neck with all her hair swept back and give him a watery salt kiss full on the mouth. Her skin tingled at the thought of it and it made her stop and try to count how many weeks it was since they had last made love. When she arrived back at the towels, running through the warm air, she sprayed Paul a little intentionally with her wet hair.

'Owww,' he winced as the icy water hit his legs. He'd opened one of the bottles of wine, pressing the cork in with his thumb. He took a long thirsty gulp and pushed the bottle into a well of sand. Anna lay down, glistening with tiny drops, and began to read her book. It was a novel, a serious novel but with a lush, unexpected strain. Newly awakened women and rampaging men. There were whole paragraphs of shameless, blistering talk.

Anna slid a little closer so that their bodies touched. There was no one about. Paul did not respond. She placed a hand on his leg and nuzzled her face into his neck.

'Anna.' Paul sat up. 'Someone could appear at any moment.'

Without speaking Anna rolled back on to her towel. She didn't want to be accused of sulking, so she kept a little flickering smile at the edges of her mouth.

A man walked on to the beach. He wore dark clothes and a felt hat and was obviously not a tourist. Paul turned to her and squeezed her breast. 'You see.'

Yes and it would have all been over by now, she thought meanly, but she said nothing. Paul jumped up and ran down to the water's edge. He threw himself in and struck out in a crawl. Anna put down her book and watched him. Even the way he moved his arm in an arc above his head was free and hurtful.

The man had walked up the beach and was standing in the shadow of the cliff wall, where deep red caves led back into the hill. Anna unpacked the picnic. She pulled at a stick of bread and sliced the cheese with a knife that she had put in with the towels and suncream in her rucksack.

When Paul came out of the water he stood over her and shook himself, and although she intended to be as irritable as he had been, she found that she was laughing.

'I wonder what he's doing up there,' Paul said, letting his eyes wander towards the man, and when Anna followed his gaze he leaned over and, running his fingers down the inside of her arm, took a bite out of her sandwich.

It was late in the afternoon when they arrived back at the port. They wandered along the sea front looking for Eduardo's diving boat. The shops, which had been closed all afternoon, were just starting to reopen, and smartly dressed men strolled leisurely along the front. They walked right along the quay until the yachts thinned and the shops stopped and the coast twisted under the huge cliffs on which the old winding town of Bonifaccio was perched. The sea had dented the cliffs in crumbling hollows so that half the town hovered on a ridge of rock that rested on thin air.

The diving boat was mooring up. Anna saw Eduardo flinging out a coil of rope. His face was golden brown, silver streaks of salt water striped his legs. Anna wandered how it was that foreign men could get away with wearing flip-flops.

'Anna.' Pip leapt ashore. 'Have you had a nice day?'

'We certainly have,' Paul answered for her. 'We had the beach all to ourselves.' He squeezed Anna's shoulder meaningfully.

Pip scowled across at Eduardo, who continued to coil his rope around the landing post.

'Has it been a good day?' Paul turned to him. But Eduardo was busy directing the divers to their hotel.

'Sure, sure,' he said.

'Take no notice.' Pip led them back to the boat for tea. 'Sometimes I'm tempted to put cyanide in his soup.'

'Has it been this bad before?' Anna asked.

'Not for a couple of weeks.' And Pip suddenly smiled. 'I

could block the toilet with a Lil-let, that would get him.' But to Anna's relief she stayed where she was.

'I just feel uncomfortable with them so close by,' Paul said half-way through the week when Anna tried to coerce him into making love to her. She was starting to feel a little panicky. If they went home without having had sex the holiday would be a failure. 'We could be very quiet?'
 Paul turned away from her and sighed.

During the days they walked up into the old town and took the paths that led away from it in all directions. They came across a disused slaughterhouse with a gully for the blood to run straight off, over the cliff. It was painted red. Paul took out his camera and focused in on it from every angle. Anna stood and watched him, even posing, smiling, by the blood-red shaft. 'I wonder if Pip and Eduardo will make up,' she said.
 They found a graveyard overgrown and entangled in a sea of weeds. Paul peered into a shrine of urns with flowers and photographs in frames arranged on shelves. Anna stretched to look at the engraved names when a huge spider scuttled down and landed on her hand. She shrieked and jerked her arms, causing such a stir that birds from all over the hill wheeled up into the air. 'It's all right,' she said, deflated. 'It was only a leaf.'

It was the first of June and so hot suddenly that they packed a picnic and walked straight to the beach. They took it in turns to swim, and when Anna was alone she glanced uncomfortably behind her for the man in the felt hat. She imagined she could see him, his hot hands hanging swollen by his sides. It was possible he was standing in the shadows of the cave, watching her look around.
 'Don't be ridiculous,' Paul said, and he dripped water in warm welts on to her book.
 Towards evening they walked home along a shaded path.

Paul pointed something out to her, and as Anna hurried to catch up, a thin dry claw caught around her leg. She gasped and almost fell, but when she looked down she saw it was a tangle of dried grass. 'Don't worry.' She bent down, but as she did so an animal dropped on to her neck. She fought it off, blind with panic, shivering and struggling to get free. There were loose flapping tendrils, a giant grasshopper, rustling in her hair. Too late, she realized it was just her empty rucksack falling forward off her back.

'I don't know what's wrong with me,' she sobbed. 'I'm having such a nice time.'

Paul put his arm around her. He kissed her ear.

When they got back to the boat music was playing and the smell of oil and frying fish coiled deliciously up on to the deck. Pip was dancing, a spatula in her hand. 'Supper will be served in the lounge at eight o'clock. Drinks anyone?' And although it wasn't nearly dark she lit two candles.

Eduardo, ruffled and half-dressed, emerged from the starboard cabin. As he slipped past Pip he slid an arm across her stomach.

'Is it nearly ready?' he grinned. 'I'm starving.'

Pip flipped her spatula and danced.

Paul and Anna took their drinks and sat up on the deck. 'Bloody mosquitoes,' Paul said, and he slapped his thigh.

'What happened?' Anna asked. Pip raised her shoulders and puckered up her lips. 'I used my womanly wiles.'

'You little minx. Minxes the lot of you.' Paul laughed.

'I wish you weren't going,' Pip said, but even as she said it she was listening for Eduardo in the shower.

'Cheer up.' Paul handed her a snorkel and mask. 'We'll be home tomorrow.'

'Yes.' Anna sat glumly on the stones, her flippers sticking up into the air.

'Can you imagine,' he said, 'being like those two? What a life.'

'Yes,' Anna said. 'How can they bear it?' She stood up and flapped down to the shore.

Paul followed and took her hand. 'Sorry I've been a bit . . . a bit distant. I've just been feeling rather . . .'

'No, it's fine, really.' It was all she needed from him. One tiny chink. Anna squeezed his hand. 'I understand.'

'I know you do.' They pulled their masks over their eyes and together with their flippered feet they kicked out into the bay where shoals of blue translucent fish skittered about beneath them.

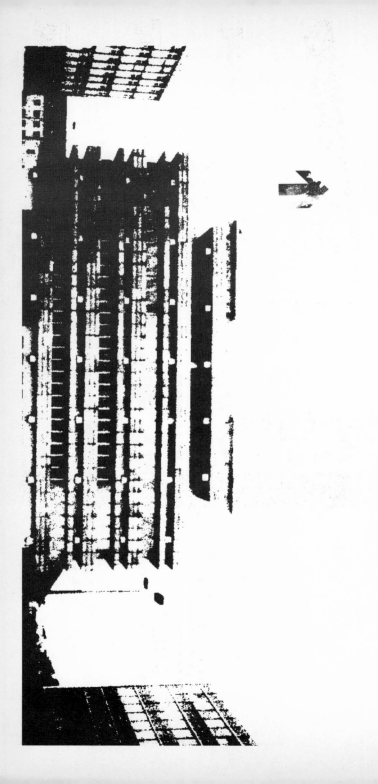

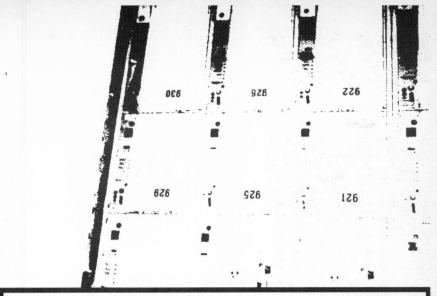

Toby Litt
My Cold War: February 1998

Toby Litt was born in 1968. He grew up in Ampthill, Bedfordshire. His first two books are a short-story collection, Adventures In Capitalism, and a novel, Beatniks. His new novel Corpsing will be published by Hamish Hamilton in early 2000.

If I hadn't been bored and friendless in Berlin, I would never have thought to search my hotel room; and if I hadn't searched, I would never have found what I found – and I would have avoided my Cold War completely. The hotel was situated near Potsdamer Platz, part of the former Democratic Republic. Before October 1989, Doppelzimmer 834 – like every other East German hotel room – would have been bugged, would have had at least *that* glamour. But on February 1st 1998, there was nothing whatsoever of interest: a mushy-springed bed, a wood-laminate wardrobe, an old-style phone, a green-brown-grey-blue carpet. And from the streets outside, beyond the sticky net curtains, came the sound of pneumatic drills – like Wagner's Siegfried multiplied and amplified. I don't know exactly why I unscrewed the white-painted plasterboard which covered the fireplace. Perhaps because my room had no television. Perhaps because the fat steel screw-heads reminded me of the rivets in the side of a ship. Perhaps simply because my Swiss Army penknife had a screwdriver attachment. Anyhow, the whole thing was loosened up in about ten minutes. There were twenty or so screws, a couple of which were a little stiff. I don't know what I was expecting to find. A radio, maybe – concealed for listening to the World Service. Pornography, perhaps. Dust and soot and cobwebs, definitely. Yet behind the plasterboard the fireplace was perfectly, almost antiseptically clean. Someone had sealed up the chimney-hole, and the same person, or so I guessed, had given everything a couple of coats of white gloss. Most remarkably of all, this person had left behind a clear plastic bag (one of the ones with an airtight seal along the edge) containing a vintage Leica. After only the slightest hesitation I picked it out of the shiny white grate. There was something very satisfying in finding – if only by accident – something that had been so meticulously hidden. It was a fulfilment, of sorts: a greater fulfilment than had come my way in many months of travel. My Cold War, although I wasn't at the time aware, had already begun.

Leaving the plasterboard propped up beside the fireplace, I walked over to the bed (the room, though boring, was surprisingly large) and sat down to examine the camera. As I unsealed the plastic bag, I sniffed the air it contained. Scentless, as far as I could tell – no aftershave, no perfume. The Leica was beautiful. I don't know a great deal about cameras but I do know that among photographers Leicas are universally admired and uniquely craved. 'When the shutter goes,' I'd heard one photojournalist acquaintance say, 'it makes no noise. You can take a person's photo –' Silence ' – and they will never know.' I'd also picked up the information (misinformation as it turned out: the comment refers to Praktikas) that Leicas were of two kinds, West and East German; and that the West German ones were far superior. I turned the Leica over, heavy but balanced in my hands. There were, of course, no external markings to tell me East or West. Somehow I was certain there must be film inside it: no way would someone, however eccentric or paranoid, hide a mere camera. It must contain information, images. And so I didn't attempt to open it.

I'd only been in the hotel two hours, but now I checked out – smuggling the Leica through reception deep within my suitcase. I paid – in cash, in full – for the room I would not be using and the breakfast I would not eat. No surprise was expressed at my so-early departure. The receptionist, sallow and lethargic, a woman, seemed incapable of expressing anything at all. Before vacating Doppelzimmer 834, I had screwed the plasterboard back over the fireplace – making everything appear as undisturbed as possible. Already I was behaving like a spy.

I moved across town. My Western hotel was a great deal

more luxurious than my Eastern. As there was no reason for me to hold back on the money, I spent a huge amount more than was necessary – and for this I got gilding, plush and an utterly dead acoustic. I'd only been slumming it before in the hope that my life would acquire some atmosphere – at second-hand. (Finding an unrenovated hotel in the East had been quite a challenge; Mitte was now swankier than Charlottenburg.) But my life was in terrible need of something. For six long months, my passport and I had lain side by side on the drum-tight bedcovers of Hyatts and Hiltons the whole world over. I had been everywhere but back home – a place where there is nothing but hotels. Ex-East Germany was a sign of my desperation: I hadn't really wanted to go there. No friends. No interest. But the idea of atmosphere had attracted me. I'd made one of my more fateful airport-decisions. The stewardess swiped my credit card. The plane took off, flew, landed. The temperature on the ground was announced as zero degrees.

By the time I had checked in to the West hotel, it was eleven-thirty. I found an all-night pharmacy. As I pulled the Leica from my suit-pocket, I saw the chemist's hard face break into boyishness. 'M3a,' he said. Instantly he assumed the camera was mine, that I'd had it for years, that it was one of my most beloved objects – a pet, almost. 'Inside, the film it has?' I asked. The chemist stared at me for a moment, realizing how wrong all his assumptions had been: I felt myself becoming that which he now beheld – a barbarian, a parvenu in possession of a little piece of perfection whose impeccable quality I could not even begin (as could he, uniquely) to appreciate. *'Jawohl,'* he said, after trying the film-winder with his thumb. 'Can you to it the development make?' *'Jawohl,'* he said, this time with irony. He wound the film on to the end then popped it out of the base of the camera. One glance. 'This film is black and white. It will take twenty-four hours.' Could I trust him? If there were something incriminating in the negatives, would he call the police? Would he print off some duplicates and attempt to blackmail

me? Would he refuse even to let me see or know what had
been in them? 'No more so fast?' *'Nein,'* he said, heavily
handing the Leica back. 'Twenty-four hours,' I said. 'Exactly.'
He did not smile. I stepped out from the white shop into the
black street.

The next day I felt like playing up to my ideas of
atmosphere, and so I went back to my Eastern hotel and
took coffee in the drab dining room. There was no sign of the
gossipy excitement and expanded curiosity that follows a visit
from the police. No one paid any undue attention to me: the
night staff and the day staff didn't much overlap. The one
person I'd spoken to before, the woman receptionist, ignored
my presence completely – at least to begin with. My own
suspicion was that the camera belonged to one of the hotel's
customers, not one of its staff. As I imagined them, he or she
(more likely he) was someone who stayed there regularly –
always requesting the same room. I wanted to ask the
receptionist if such a person existed, but my German was too
poor to pass off such an enquiry with the requisite
nonchalance. Attention would be drawn to me, unnecessary
attention. In fact, the receptionist was even now having a
word with the elderly concierge whilst looking in my direction.
Perhaps she did, after all, recognize me. I nodded to the
head waiter as I walked quickly out.

Exactly twenty-four hours after leaving it, I returned to the
all-night pharmacy. The chemist handed over the paper
wallet of developed photographs. His face gave no clue as to
what I would find when I opened it. The charge for developing
the film seemed exorbitant. I wanted to ask if it was a
standard rate, but decided against it: any dispute would
make the chemist even more likely to remember me –
something I was still hoping to avoid.

Just down the street from the all-night pharmacy a
night-club was open. Once inside, I found a deep booth,
ordered a beer and – after waiting for it to arrive, then waiting
a little longer for the waiter to go away – opened the wallet.
The instant I saw the photographs, I knew that I was in

danger: I had interrupted something – some mad
pan-European project. The film-roll had been twenty-four
frames long. There were fourteen exposed images. Each
photograph was of a roadsign, taken from roughly the same
distance away (I imagined the photographer pacing out the
gap) – and every roadsign was for a different European city. It
was simply unbelievable. I cannot convey the shock that
these images gave me – so simple, so repetitious. Careful not
to disturb their order (although I could always check back
with the negatives), I wrote down the following list: Berlin,
Copenhagen, Amsterdam, Luxemburg, Brussels, Paris,
London, Rome, Dublin, Athens, Madrid, Lisbon, Bonn, Vichy.

It was the final two names on the list which gave me the
clue I needed: Bonn, the disputed capital of Germany; Vichy,
the capital of Nazi-occupied France. The photographer had
already taken photographs of all the capital cities of the
European Union. Now, they were journeying into history –
capitals that might have been, capitals that were but failed.
This second half of the project (shots thirteen to twenty-four)
seemed only just to have begun. But did the figure
twenty-four have any greater significance? Was it merely the
number of exposures on this particular roll of film? Of which
signposts, of which capital cities, were the next ten
photographs to be taken? Was the project's incompletion
due to lack of time, or money, or was there some less
guessable obstacle? I took a couple of moments to compare
my recent random wanderings with the utterly logical itinerary
of this traveller. Who were they? It had to be a man, surely.
No woman would do something so pointless in its obedience
to arbitrary rules – a woman would need an emotional motive
for such a project. Examining the photographs one by one, I
searched for a clue to the photographer's identity. But his
shadow was not cast on to the signposts nor upon the
ground; his reflection was not betrayed by a single shiny
surface. The photographer seemed entirely absent from his
photographs. I wondered, Why signposts? Why not obvious
landmarks: Big Ben, the Eiffel Tower, the Little Mermaid, the

Parthenon? Perhaps because signposts are less deniable. Perhaps because I was dealing with a madman. The variations between signpost-photographs were delicious: the ground, dusty-white outside Athens, grassy-grey outside Brussels. London had been taken against a background of fog, Lisbon was slightly over-exposed.

Looking again and again at the photographs – slowly, quickly, now rearranging them (alphabetically, dark to light), now dealing them like cards – I slowly began to see something that should have been obvious before: in two of them (Dublin and London) the road was to the right of the signpost, whereas in all the others it was to the left. I noticed something else: a white Volkswagen Beetle appeared in the background of both these photographs. There must be a reason for this: I tried to envisage it. The photographer's working method was unvarying – he always approached the signpost in the same way, parking at the same distance. Because of the eccentric English and Irish habit of driving on the left side of the road, the photographer's method had been slightly disrupted. And because of this, he had unwittingly included a trace of himself in these two photographs. I had my clue: a white Volkswagen Beetle, right-hand drive and with German number-plates.

When I got back to my West hotel room, the inevitable: it had been searched. The contents of my suitcase had been tipped out on to the bed. The wardrobe doors were ripped off their hinges. The chest of drawers was pulled away from the wall. Even the phone had been taken apart. Luckily, I had placed the Leica in the hotel safe. Although I did not know it at the time, my Cold War had just escalated. I sat down on the edge of the double bed. How had the photographer found me? Probably he'd spotted me when I returned to the first hotel. How stupid I'd been to go back there! I ran my hands up into my hair. I could feel it turning grey, becoming brittle. Should I change hotel? If so, the photographer would be bound to follow me again. Did I want to force a confrontation so soon?

I phoned down to reception and had the concierge send up some cigarettes. When the bellboy came through the door, he glanced around the room with an expression that somehow managed to be both impeccably deadpan and deeply ironic. I had seen this young man before: he'd been the one who had carried my single suitcase up to my room. He had a very podgy-pasty face and hair that, whilst being too close-cropped to merit managerial censure, stood insolently vertical. He was annoying, intimidating and curiously attractive – and didn't he know it. I felt uneasy, and he knew that the longer he lingered in my unease the larger his tip would be. 'Cigarettes,' I said. The bellboy handed them over, taking the opportunity to advance further into the room, my unease. 'Is everything all right, sir?' he asked. I forced myself to tip him. 'You have lost something?' he said. 'Cigarettes,' I said. 'I lost cigarettes.' He nodded, then performed his patented discreet-retreat.

The bellboy's formality whilst in the room gave me an idea: the photographer, whoever he was, had proven himself to be a deeply meticulous individual. Yet the searching of my room had been uncontrolled, almost wild. And whilst this contradiction might not mean anything (perhaps I had merely infuriated a normally placid temperament), it *was* highly suggestive. On an impulse I turned off the room lights, went over to the window and glanced out through the curtains. Unbelievable: parked directly opposite the hotel was a white Volkswagen Beetle.

I charged out of my room, sprinted down the corridor and pressed for the lift. It took for ever to arrive – and when it did it was full of fat old men in Lederhosen. They took their time ballooning out into the corridor. Once inside the lift, I pressed for the ground floor. It started to descend. So slowly – I hadn't noticed how slow the lift was before. As I rushed out into the lobby, I practically knocked the bellboy over coming the other way. I apologized, and kept on going. 'Excuse me, sir,' he shouted. 'Excuse me.' People in the foyer were looking round – old ladies. I had to turn back, couldn't just run out into the street. 'My apologies, sir. But I forgot to ask you to sign for the cigarettes. If you could just . . .' I signed the receipt. 'Thank you, sir.' By the time I burst out into the cool night air of Berlin, the Volkswagen was gone.

I went back up to my room, forlorn. The door was still open and the lights were off. When I turned them on, I spotted the unopened cigarette packet lying on the floor by the window – just where I'd dropped it before running out. I slouched over, picked it up, cracked it open. That was strange – no Cellophane wrapper. I quickly counted the white circles of the filters: twenty. Perhaps the bellboy was making a few extra DMs by filling the hotel's branded packs with cheap no-brand fags of his own. I pulled the cigarettes out, intending to check the filters for the maker's name – but as I was doing so, a white oblong card fell out on to the carpet. After stuffing all but one of the cigarettes back into the packet, I bent down to pick the card up. There was a message on it, typed out on an old manual typewriter. The message (in German) read:

Tomorrow. Staatsoper. 6pm. Tristan und Isolde.
A ticket will be reserved under your name.
Bring the photographs and the negatives.
Wear your black suit. Buy a new tie: blue silk.

I had two suits: one grey, one black. Since arriving in Berlin, I had worn only the grey. The black suit, along with everything else that had been in my suitcase, now lay tipped out on my hotel bed. How had the photographer known that I owned a black suit? I thought back to the first hotel. I hadn't even opened my suitcase there. The only people who might know I owned a black suit were whoever had searched my room and the bellboy. I followed this line of thought: the bellboy was the one who had been bringing me the message in the cigarette pack; the bellboy had prevented me from running out into the street after the Volkswagen; the bellboy must know something, even if he didn't know everything. I called down to reception and had the concierge send up a double vodka. But the bellboy who brought it wasn't the same as before. This was an old man with the milky-blue eyes of an alcoholic. 'Where is he?' I asked. 'The other bellboy? I wanted him.' I didn't mind being taken for a homosexual. 'Sir, arrangements can be made . . .' 'Bring him to me.' 'But, sir, he has gone off duty. I am on duty now. Would you like something else?' He winked. 'Something young?' 'I need to speak to the bellboy. Where is he?' 'He has gone home.' 'Where does he live?' 'Sir, I cannot say.' I took out my wallet and extracted a high-denomination note. 'I need to speak to him.' The old man looked from side to side, then whispered: 'Sometimes after work he goes to drink in the Stalin Bar on Bergmannstrasse. I will say nothing more.' I gave him the note and let him go.

A taxi took me to the Stalin Bar. Sure enough, the entire room was full of huge portraits of Our Great Fraternal Leader: Stalin-stern being applauded in the munitions factory; Stalin-beaming paying a surprise visit to the collective farm; Stalin-businesslike boarding a chuffing steam-train; Stalin-vigilant at his desk late into the perilous night. The tables were crowded, full of young people – drinking and smoking, laughing and talking. This was the first time since arriving in Berlin that I'd encountered such a cacophony of the German language. These boys and girls were *really* using Deutsch to communicate – not just pretending to speak it, whilst abroad, to scare foreigners off from visiting their country. I felt nauseous, wanted to sit down, drink. But I went ahead, searching the room for the bellboy. He wasn't at any of the crowded tables. I sat down at the bar, intending to wait and see if he would turn up later. I had nothing else to do. 'What'll it be, comrade?' the barman asked. 'Vodka,' I was just about to say, when I caught sight of the bellboy in the mirror behind the bar.

I spun round on my stool to confront him. 'Hey!' I said. Instantly, he panicked. As he dashed for the door I stepped into his path – but he merely lowered his shoulder and

shunted me out of the way. I fell back, sprawling against the
bar stools, watching helplessly as he dodged between the
tables and out into the street. Although I knew there was no
way I'd be able to catch up, I ran out after him. He was
already a hundred yards off, sprinting without looking back.
'Hey!' I shouted, pointlessly.

Back at the hotel I asked to see the manager. He was fat
and efficient. His uniform was neatly creased but because
none of the creases fell in straight lines it made him look
scruffy rather than smart. He did not sweat or mop his bald
brow with a handkerchief (no nervous fat-man clichés). 'Who
was the bellboy who came up to my room just now?' He
checked with a subordinate. 'That was Mark Felm. Have you
a complaint about the service which you received from him?'
'No, but I need to speak to him.' 'I'm sure I can help you, sir.'
'Where does he live?' 'It is not hotel policy to disclose
personal information about either our guests *or* our
employees.' 'I'm not gay, if that's what you're thinking.'
'Sir . . .' 'Please.' 'Mark Felm only began working here
yesterday. If you have any complaint to make against him, it
will be treated with the greatest of seriousness. He came with
the highest references.' I gave up and went to bed.

Sometimes – though rarely – what one anticipates one
encounters; and, rarer still, the anticipated fails to disappoint.
The Staatsoper was an imposing neo-classical building in
ugly stone. Black pollution-streaks ran down the statues
above its portico. My seat was about half-way back in the
stalls, at the end of a row. And there she was – my
anticipated – beautiful and aloof – sitting in the seat beside
mine. Wordlessly, I sat beside her; I would wait for *her* to
speak – she would be the one to set the tone. Yet it was only
now, when I had looked away from her and up towards the
grand gaudy fire curtain that I realized I had seen this woman
before – in Berlin. But where? I couldn't remember having
seen anyone so beautiful. And then I knew – because she
hadn't been as beautiful the last time I saw her: she was the
receptionist from my East German hotel. All the greyness had

gone from her, and all the care. She shone where she had
been dull, energy had replaced torpor. I turned to look at her,
to confirm. Yes, I'd been correct – but at that exact moment
Wagner's Prelude swelled up, seasick and miraculous. The
receptionist gazed steadily towards the stage, the unraised
curtain. I did not seem to exist for her, not right now, not
quite yet.

It has been said that *Tristan und Isolde* is the sexiest work
of art ever created. I knew the opera very well, and was
hoping to have established some intimacy with the
receptionist during the interval – the better to enjoy the
by-proxy foreplay of Act II. It was the first time my erotic
curiosity had been stimulated in months.

As the moment drew closer and closer I became more and
more agitated. When the lights came up, the receptionist was
the first person in the entire auditorium to get to her feet. I
stood up, too – along with almost everyone else. The
receptionist pushed past me, then turned her head slightly.
'Follow me,' she said, moving her lips as little as possible. No
introduction. No names. Hardly even a glance. Hurriedly, she
pushed her way out of the auditorium. I did my best to keep
up – mortally offending several camp Wagnerites in the
process. Once into the corridor, the receptionist headed
straight for one of the fire doors. I went after her, finding that
it led directly out into the chill Berlin night. All of a sudden, we
were alone. 'What is your name?' I asked. 'Come here,' she
said, walking towards a darker part of the alley. Behind us,
someone else came out of the Staatsoper fire door. For a
brief moment the alley was lit up – and I saw two men waiting
in the shadow that the receptionist had been beckoning me
towards. One of the men I recognized: the bellboy; the other
I'd never seen before. He was an older man, fifty-plus, with
hard eyes and an even harder jawline. My first thought was
that it was the receptionist and not myself who was in
danger. 'Hey,' I shouted. 'Come back!' They rushed me
before I had time even to gasp; the old man moving with
surprising speed. A rough hessian sack was pulled over my

head and my hands were twistingly cuffed. I was hustled
further into the shadows (I could still, through the sacking,
make out the difference between light and dark), a sharp
blow met the back of my skull and I was swallowed by the
exploding pain and engulfing unconsciousness. The last thing
I heard was the receptionist's voice saying: 'My name is
Isolde.'

When I came to I was lying flat, being bumped and slid
around, in complete darkness, a car engine booming and
road noise hushing. Where were they taking me? The
handcuffs dug into my wrists. My legs, too, had been put
under restraint. Although I could see nothing, my head was
starry with pain. After a particularly huge supernova of agony,
I again lost consciousness.

The next time I awoke, I was tied to a chair in a damp
cellar, being blasted with light from three halogen lamps.
Isolde – if that was really her name – had just slapped me a
couple of times, hard, to bring me round. My blindfold had
been removed, probably by Isolde. The bellboy and the older
man were standing to one side, smoking. My back was
soaked with sweat. My clothes smelt of petrol. Isolde, on
seeing that I was again conscious, stood up and stepped
back from me. As she moved, I caught her perfume – it came
to me as gently as a promise (perhaps a false promise). If I
were to survive this, whatever it was – a prospect that
seemed fairly unlikely – then I might again, with Isolde or with
some other woman, share a close-up world of scent,
softness and safety. But that seemed a long way off, a
memory of the future. I could not speak: my mouth was
tightly gagged. Isolde approached the two men and spoke to
them in a low voice. I was having trouble focusing, with the
unbearable light and the sweat falling into my eyes – but I
saw the hard-faced man hand Isolde a cigarette. The bellboy
lit it for her, gallantly, with a flashing silver cigarette lighter.
Isolde was wearing a long raincoat with the collar turned up.
After a deep drag, she walked back towards me. 'I am about
to remove your gag. If you scream, no one will hear – no one

except Mark and Melot. Mark will probably kick you in the
face; Melot will do something far more subtle and far more
painful. Nod once if you understand.' She had a beautiful
voice, even in its harshness. I nodded once. Isolde tore off
the gag.

The delight of easy air itself almost made me scream.
Instead, I gasped animal for a while. Isolde smoked, her ash
falling wispy-dark through the light. Despite my gasping, I
wanted that cigarette. 'The negatives,' she said. 'Tell me
where they are.' I was in no mood to resist. After I'd regained
my breath, I said, 'They are in the safe, in my hotel.' Isolde
turned to Mark, the bellboy. In rapid German, she asked him
a question, to which he replied, *'Nein.'* 'Why did you not
bring them?' Isolde asked. 'I didn't know . . .' I said. 'What?'
she snapped. 'That they were for you,' I said. 'If I had, I would
have brought them.' Isolde stood as a thin shadow between
the three bright lights.

Suddenly the old man grabbed her. He was shouting in
German, furious, twisting her neck. She started to gasp,
fighting back. One of the lights was knocked over in the
struggle. The bellboy helped to subdue her. His loyalties were
obvious. 'Stop!' I shouted. 'Don't hurt her!' 'What?' said the
old man into the air. Then he turned to me. 'Leave her alone!'
I cried. 'I'll give you the negatives – just don't hurt her!' 'Isolde
has failed,' he said. 'She promised us the photographs and
the negatives. We are very angry. Mark cannot get them from
the hotel safe, only the manager has the keys. But you will
bring the negatives to the Brandenburg Gate, tomorrow, at
midnight. Remember this. Midnight. If you and the negatives
are not there, you will never see this pretty one again. Nor will
anyone else.' The old man now had Isolde completely
subdued. The bellboy stepped behind me, lifted his cosh,
and the lights went out.

The next time I woke up I was lying on soft wet earth in the
middle of a forest. Rain was swishing into the thick pine
branches over my aching head. There was no gag on my
mouth or blindfold over my eyes. My wrists and ankles felt as

bad as if I'd been crucified. I tried to stand up, fell over, tried again, fell against a tree-trunk and grasped it for support. This seemed my only way of progressing, though where I was intending to go I had no idea.

Blindly, I stumbled onwards, for what seemed like hours. My rescue was at first an inconvenience: I came to a place where there was a larger than usual gap between trees. I lurched forwards, my ankles screaming with agony. Nothing for me to flop against. I fell to the ground, which wasn't ground, which was harder than that, much harder. Somehow, I'd happened upon a road. Before this thought had time to sink in, I heard a car-engine approaching – then saw lights getting bigger, getting closer. I pushed myself up, exhausted, grazing my hands on the gritted Tarmac. One knee, the other – and push: up: now. I was standing. I knew if I tried to get off the road I would simply fall over again, the driver wouldn't see me and I'd be run over, killed. It seemed safer just to stand there, arms out to either side, pleading for survival and deliverance. The car came rapidly around the bend – a dipping of the front left wheel the first indication that the driver had seen me. But would they be able to stop soon enough to avoid hitting me? No: no stopping, no time – so they swerved past me, the side mirror tapping my thigh. The car was a silver-white Mercedes 106e. Now that there was a possibility of deliverance, the rain on my face started to feel good. I didn't have the strength or balance to turn around. I could hear the Mercedes' gull-wing door opening, upwards and outwards. German was being spoken – aggressive, male. Like a scarecrow I stood there, cruciform, unterrifying. The shouting continued. A hand was placed firmly on my shoulder. It was too much for me to bear – I fell straight to the ground, blacking out.

This time when I woke up it was far more pleasant than before. At first all I was aware of was the softness against my skin – the softness I had been promised by Isolde's perfume – the softness, as it turned out, of a pair of black silk pyjamas. I had survived. Here I was. In a large white bed. (I got up.) In a large white room. (I walked downstairs and out into the drive.) In a large white house. (I turned all around.) On the very edge of a large black lake. The pyjamas belonged to the owner of the silver-white Mercedes – a man whose name I never found out. He had dumped me at his country villa and left me for the servants to deal with. There was an English butler, a French maid and a Brazilian chauffeur. The butler dressed me, the maid fed me and the chauffeur drove me back to Berlin. (If it hadn't happened to me, I would have believed it was a dream. Thank you, Germany. After all, I discover that you have a believable heart – a huge one, beating for me, for other helpless ones, too.) The white house by the black lake was two hours from Berlin – to the south. We took the Rolls-Royce, black, shiny. The chauffeur was handsome, dark-eyed, and smiled slowly at my questions: 'Where did he find me?' and 'How far did he have to bring me to get here?' and 'When can I see him to thank him?' The chauffeur knew – or pretended to know – nothing of the circumstances in which his master had discovered me. 'The master likes to drive himself sometimes' – that was all he would say. The bridges on the autobahn blip-blip-blipped past at over 120 m.p.h.

I hadn't woken up until four in the afternoon. We didn't set off for Berlin until six. It was a quarter past eight when the Rolls-Royce dropped me off outside my hotel. The chauffeur got out and opened the door for me, as if I were royalty; then he got back in and drove off without a backwards glance, as if I were something unpleasant he'd dumped on a tip. I walked into the hotel lobby, looking out for the bellboy, Mark, who I knew wouldn't be there. Although my old black suit was now lying in a dustbin somewhere close to the Swiss border, I instinctively checked the pockets of my new black suit for my room key. (Sometimes we owe our stupidity more than we owe intelligence.) Of course, it wasn't there – but something else was: a key with a locker number on it and the words 'Zoo station' written around it.

The manager stood behind the reception desk. As I

approached him, he looked confused by the contradictory
signals I was giving out: injured face and hands, immaculate
tailoring. In English, I asked him to get my things from the
safe. It was lucky he didn't ask me for identification. The suit
took care of the formalities. The manager, it seemed, had
misjudged me. In a moment he handed over the envelope
containing the negatives and the set of photographs. After
going upstairs to fetch some money, I took the photographs
to a copy-shop, colour-photocopied them, put the
photocopies in an envelope and posted them to my
almost-forgotten home address. They came out badly but I
didn't care: I still possessed them, in some form at least. It
was ten o'clock by the time I'd finished this errand. With
nothing else to do before the exchange, and with a natural
curiosity, I hailed a taxi and told it to take me to the Zoo
station. I held the locker key between thumb and forefinger,
tapping it inquisitively on my lips.

I must have been developing new instincts by now, picking
up Cold War habits, for I had not been in the taxi longer than
a minute before I glanced through the back window to see if I
was being shadowed – and there it was, two cars behind: the
white Volkswagen Beetle. As we stopped at some
traffic-lights and it drew closer, I was able to identify the
driver: Mark, the bellboy. I didn't know what to do. The
taxi-driver was likely to think me mad if I told him to lose the
car that was following me. Also, I doubted whether my
conversational German was up to the task. The white Beetle,
as I watched it, kept an even distance – never further than
three cars away, never closer than one. Thinking as quickly
as I could, I ordered the driver to take me back to the hotel.
He turned around, and so did the white Beetle. I told the
taxi-driver to hurry; I hoped he would put a little distance
between us and Mark.

Once we arrived back at the hotel, I dashed out of the taxi
and through the soft-carpeted lobby. Into the lift and up to
my room. Without turning on the room lights or moving the
curtains, I looked down into the street. The Beetle was there,

reversing into a parking space. I phoned down to reception and asked to speak to the manager, urgently. 'Yes, sir,' he said when – after an agonizing minute – he was able to come to the phone. 'Do you have a back entrance?' I asked. 'I can't go out the front door.' 'I'm sorry, sir. The only way to leave the building is through that door.' 'What about fire exits?' I said. 'There is the roof, but –' he said. It was all I needed. I took the lift to the top floor. The fire exit wasn't hard to find. I pushed down the aluminium bar and was quickly outside. Moving carefully away from the front of the building, I looked for some way down. There was only one: a ladder, dropping vertically into the alley beside the hotel; eight floors down. And the alley led directly out into the street where Mark was waiting and watching. If I left that way the chances were he'd catch sight of me. With no immediate ideas of escape occurring to me, I went back down to my room.

I lay on the bed, blowing smoke-rings up at the ceiling. The sight of them dispersing and dissolving the higher they got was what gave me the idea. Out in the corridor, it was the job of a moment to start the fire alarm – smashing the glass with my elbow and pressing the black button. Bells rang immediately, horribly loudly. I ran back into my room, looked out of the window. Mark, I could see, was no longer in the Beetle – he had left it behind, the driver's door hanging open. Now came the gamble: I guessed that Mark would guess that I'd have tried to find some way out of the hotel other than the front door. I guessed that he'd assume I'd found the fire exit on to the roof. I guessed that he'd cover that escape route rather than the front door. And so, I went back into the corridor, descended the stairs to the lobby and traipsed out into the street with all the frightened others. My guess was wrong – Mark was back in the car, patiently keeping an eye on both exits. But as luck had it, the crush of people vacating the hotel was blocking up the road. I took my chance and ran for it. Mark saw me, got out of the Beetle. I sprinted, turned down the next street along. I dashed left, right, right again. I ducked into a sex shop and pretended to look at lingerie. I had lost him. After waiting five minutes among the frilly things (I thought of buying something black for Isolde), I stepped outside and hailed a taxi. 'Zoo station,' I said.

Sometimes – very rarely – one's life is altered in a moment; and, even more rarely, that alteration is for the better. I found the locker without difficulty; I opened it without hesitation. When I closed it, a few seconds later, with a deliberate lack of haste, I was a different man. The locker contained two things; two brown-paper envelopes, padded. I opened the top, larger one: it contained a thick stack of high-denomination Deutschmarks; I opened the second one: it contained a well-oiled revolver. Obviously, these were things one couldn't just carry away in one's hands. I locked them back up again and went off to look round the station. I found a shop selling luggage and bought myself a plain black briefcase. So paranoid had I become that I believed both the money and the gun would be gone by the time I got back to the locker. In general, I wasn't wrong to be paranoid (plots of which I was unaware were in the offing), but in this case my paranoia was misplaced. I stuffed the envelopes into the new briefcase. In the nearby gentlemen's toilets, I took the gun from its envelope, checked that it was loaded, put it in my side pocket.

Glancing at my watch, I saw that it was almost eleven. I was hungry, despite the ministrations of the French maid. In the station café, I consumed a tasteless Wiener schnitzel with over-sweetened potato salad and watery sauerkraut. A couple of beers, and I almost believed that I would use the gun – if there was any sign of trouble during the swap.

Eleven fifty-five found me approaching the Brandenburg Gate through well-lit modern streets. All around me, people went on with their normal midnight business; I, on the other hand, was embarked upon a deadly enterprise. It was hard to believe what I was about to do – to exchange a mysterious and beautiful set of photographs for a mysterious and beautiful woman. Halogen lamps whitely illuminated the Gate. There was a slight mist upon the ground. At almost exactly

twelve, a thin rain began to fall. I stood there, waiting –
unsure which way to look. Death could come at me from any
of the 360 degrees, or from above, or below. My right hand
clutched the shape of the revolver through the expensive
material of my suit – there it was, bumping solidly against my
right thigh.

Then I saw it: the white Volkswagen Beetle. As it drew
closer, I could see that the old man, Melot, was driving whilst
Mark sat in the back with Isolde. Her eyes flashed, wide and
white with terror. A couple of times the Beetle drove past the
Gate, checking that the coast was clear – and then it pulled
up ten feet or so away from me. 'You have everything with
you – the photographs and the negatives?' said the old man,
leaning out the driver's window. 'I do,' I said. 'Now let her
go!' The car jerked forwards, startlingly, then even more
abruptly halted. The back door opened and Isolde tumbled
out on to the hard cobblestone pavement. I had to restrain
the impulse to run forwards and help her to her feet. The old
man had got out on the other side of the car. Isolde's hands
were tied behind her back. Mark jumped out of the car after
her and hauled her roughly to her feet. I stood in front of the
Beetle, slightly to the side of the headlights. The briefcase felt
light in my hand, though I knew that it contained the heft of
my entire future.

'First the photographs,' said Mark, the air pluming from his
mouth. 'No,' I said. 'First the girl.' 'Why should we trust you?'
shouted the old man. I pulled the envelope containing the
photographs and the negatives out of my breast pocket. (I'd
been careful not to place them inside the briefcase.) 'I have
something you want.' Mark put his thick arm around Isolde's
neck and made as if to strangle her. 'So do we!' he shouted
in reply. 'Take off her gag,' I said. The two men consulted.
Then the old man ripped it off mercilessly. I waited a moment
for Isolde to regain her breath. 'Are you all right?' I shouted.
'All right,' she gasped, almost as if it were not an answer for
me but a question for herself. 'Should I trust them?' She
looked despairingly from one to the other. 'You'll have to.

You have no choice.' My heart was thumping. Now was my moment. 'Oh, yes, I have,' I said, and pulled the gun out of my pocket. First I pointed it at the old man. On the instant, he started to cower and beg, soiling himself. Then I let Mark feel the gun's hot beam of damage and death. He instinctively hid himself behind Isolde. There was some furious whispering amongst the three of them. The only thing I could catch was Mark saying, 'Where did he get a gun?'

'Untie her hands,' I said. 'Let her come to me.' And then Isolde said my name, gently. 'Put the gun away,' she said. Mark was uncuffing her hands. 'Point it at the ground.' The old man was running for the shelter of the Beetle. 'Be sensible.' Isolde was walking towards me. 'This is for you,' I said, and tossed the envelope at Mark. But Isolde leapt in the air – far more athletically than she should have if she'd really been tied up for twenty-four hours – and she caught it. 'No,' said Isolde. 'These are for me.' Mark's hand went to his pocket: a gun, I thought. 'Get down,' I shouted to Isolde. But she was walking steadily towards me, holding my gaze, speaking slowly. 'Listen. You don't understand what's going on. Put the gun away. I'll explain.' We were linked together – the gun pointing from me through Isolde into Mark. 'Take your hand out of your pocket,' I said to Mark. Slowly, he withdrew it – along with a set of car keys. Isolde was now standing within touching distance. 'They have no weapons,' she said. 'They would never hurt you. Mark is my brother. Melot is my father. They are not called Mark and Melot. But I *am* called Isolde.' She put her forefinger over the revolver's barrel, as if over the lips of a fractious boy, saying *shhh*, saying *all right*, saying *love*. I dropped the gun to my side, trusting her. 'Very good,' said Isolde, and put her arm through mine. 'Come with me,' she whispered. 'I'll explain everything.'

I let her lead me away from the white Beetle, through the dark streets, towards her bedroom, into the morning.

*

This is what Isolde said as she walked with me, held my
hand, took me to where she lived, kissed me, made me
coffee, kissed me again, took me to her bedroom, undressed
in front of me, undressed me: 'Once, a long time ago, in a
different time, I had a boyfriend. His name was Richard. He
was handsome and funny. He was an artist: a photographer.
His subject was landscapes. But, under the old regime, he
was not allowed to travel. None of us were. We were very
young. He was ambitious. Because he could not travel, he
wanted to go everywhere. It frustrated him terribly. And so he
conceived his project: he would smuggle a camera out of the
country and, by getting instructions to photographer friends
and acquaintances, he would have a series of photographs
taken. Each of these photographs would prove conclusively
that the camera had been to that particular country. It was his
great idea to photograph only city signs outside cities, not
famous monuments inside them. He imagined an
underground exhibition of all twenty-four photographs. And
they would be saying, 'Look, we can travel to the borders but
we cannot pass over. We have the words, the signs, but we
haven't got the images. We cannot take photographs of the
things we want to.' It would be pure and political. And so he
sent the camera, a Leica, out with a friend who came from
West Germany. He took the first five photographs: Berlin,
Copenhagen, Amsterdam, Luxemburg, Brussels. Every time
he took a photograph he sent us a postcard from that city.
Then he passed the Leica on to a French photographer. She
took Paris, London. Then she split up with her boyfriend, and
the camera was lost for a while. Then they got back together,
and she found it again. She passed it on to a Spanish
photographer, someone reliable, she said. We didn't hear
anything for a whole year. And then the postcards started to
arrive: Rome, Dublin, Athens. The Spaniard explained that he
had been saving the money to travel. He was very poor, but
this project had given him a reason to work. He is now quite
famous, I believe. In Athens, he met the woman who is now
his wife. Together they took Madrid and Lisbon. Those were

the first twelve photographs. It had taken three and a half years. Richard decided that that was enough, with the postcards, for a first underground show. (He had a second idea: for cities that had once been capitals but were no longer.) So, he asked for them to get the camera back to his West German photographer friend. Little did we know that his friend was now working in the grey area. He set himself up to be searched at the border, all the time looking innocent to us. But the Stasi got the camera and Richard never saw the photographs. He was arrested, when it became clear what he had done. There was a short and meaningless trial. Richard spent a year in prison. After he came out, he lost all hope. He was being watched. He had lost his most trusted friend. He said he no longer loved me, though I knew he did. And he caught pneumonia and did not look after himself properly and he lay in bed and died.'

Then she stopped speaking and we made love. And then this is what Isolde said, as we lay side by side, holding hands, touched, kissed, watched the ceiling go grey, kissed again, fell asleep: 'When Richard died I was distraught. I myself wanted to die, to follow him. He had died so soon before things changed. That made things worse. But it did give me the reason to live – to see if I could now complete the project in Richard's memory. I worked in the hotel, I saved, I bought a Leica, I travelled when I could, I took the twelve photographs. Then I went on to the next stage: the imaginary capitals. I had just begun. In between times, I hid the camera behind the fireplace in the hotel room that had been where Mark and I met to talk. At first, I didn't know why. There was no Stasi any more. No one to be scared of. But I wanted to continue the conditions of secrecy. Also, I was lonely in my game. I wanted someone to join me. For me the Cold War wouldn't be over until I had completed Richard's project. I was still in mourning. But someone could help me, travel with me. But only someone who was still in the same world as I was. I knew that anyone who would search their room so thoroughly that they would unscrew the fireplace would be the one. So, I left the Leica there. And anyone who looked likely, I put them in that room. Mostly men, but not all. I had great hopes for you – from the moment you checked in. The room was still bugged from before. I had arranged with my father and my brother to perform the series of tests upon you. And you came through all of them, wonderfully. It was clear that you immediately understood where you were – that you were fighting your own Cold War. You became a spy so delightfully easily. You even managed to get hold of a gun. But now, thanks to you, my Cold War is perhaps over.'

When I woke up late that afternoon, Isolde was gone. But she had left something behind for me, a hint – in the dent in the pillow in which her head had so recently lain there now lay a postcard: Lenin, in wax or embalmed, in his mausoleum, in Moscow.

We thank y

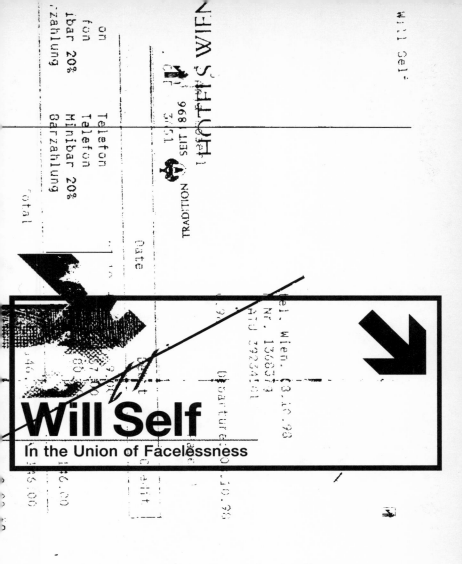

Will Self
In the Union of Facelessness

Will Self is the author of The Quantity Theory of Insanity, one of the most acclaimed debuts of 1991 and winner of the 1992 Geoffrey Faber Memorial Prize; the highly original novellas Cock & Bull; Grey Area, a second collection of short stories; Junk Mail, a selection of other works; My Idea of Fun and Great Apes, his well-received novels; and a third short-story collection, Tough, Tough Toys for Tough, Tough Boys. All of these are published in

Penguin

John had found Vienna to be even more absurd than he remembered. The name was a problem to begin with: in German 'Wien'; hence wiener; hence – when he was growing up, a queerly half-Jewish child in seventies London – 'Vienna'. His pukka Jew friends at school would say: 'I'm just going to get a Vienna and some chips . . .' Or would they? Gross God.

They also – perhaps because of phylogenetic memories of the East End – would say: 'Wally'; as in 'I'm just going to get a wally and some chips . . .' A wally was a pickled gherkin – or was it? Gross God.

In the caf' at the airport, where John was served with a travesty of a cappuccino: cumuli of cream towering over a slop of caffeine (and yet Austrians were meant to be so fucking proud of their coffee, or were they? Gross God), another man's mobile phone rang. The peal was the opening chords of *Eine Kleine Nacht Musik* – or was it? Because even as it beeped annoyance at John, and the Austrian's pig visage crumpled into acquiescence, he found that he could no longer remember what the opening chords of *Eine Kleine Nacht Musik* were. The piece, once profoundly loved by him, had become little more than a student race memory, compounded with bedsits, Nescafé and fumbled sex.

He had said to the driver of the slightly stretch Merc': 'I'm not going to go to Frankfurt, I'm going to go to South America, begin a new life'; and they'd talked about Brazil – which the driver had visited – and they both opined that the Brazilians were crazy, both tapped their foreheads with their index fingers in the *lingua franca* of derision.

John was half-serious about this, because ever since arriving in Vienna, things had begun to go wrong. Everywhere in the city there were underwear and lingerie shops, displaying billboards on which demure and inaccessible young ladies paraded their twenty-foot long pudenda; their breasts like bubble cars. Even if he could have scored with these women, it would have been a failure; his little wiener would be lost, wandering among these illimitable alps and valleys of erectile tissue. Or so John imagined.

Anyway, it was a taunt; another act by Gross God. John's Vienna was so unsalient, so ingrown; he might – he supposed – be an incipient victim of *latah*, the Malaysian hysterical condition, whereby victims became convinced that their penis was about to shrink inside their body. Those foolish Malays would get exercised about the telescoping of their manhood; and resort to absurd stratagems, such as tying it to the inside of their thigh – or even nailing it! Not John. He couldn't give – or receive – a toss. His sexuality had become a matter for purely academic concern: did it exist at all? And if so, how could it be observed with any objectivity?

In Brazil John would have plastic surgery (just for the hell of it – he wasn't concerned about pursuit) and start a business. Something solid enough – perhaps wholesale – and dull; beautifully dull. John had a hunch he was good at business – he had a spreadsheet in his head. It would be so refreshing after the bogus pavane of his career thus far.

Anyway, what was his career? John stared at the dollop of cream atop his coffee. He couldn't . . . remember. He knew he was on his way to Frankfurt to attend a trade show, but what the trade was – he was passively bemused to realize – he had no idea. It was like a conceit for some story; sitting here in Vienna airport with his identity steadily eroding. Perhaps it was the Central European context? Traditionally the English looked for their anonymity in the American heartland – just another example of the special relationship – but recently depersonalization was to be found closer to home, in the European Union of Facelessness. To his left another mobile rang. This time it was *Thus Spake Zarathustra*. Gross God.

He was losing his identity. It was a fictional conceit –
perhaps he was a writer? Certainly, John acknowledged, he
had a manifest penchant for seeking out the telling phrase,
the *mot juste*, the precise aperçu. Only minutes before he
had partially relieved himself in a *toiletten*; and after the
deluge risen to see a gleaming pretzel of shit, elegantly furled
on a purpose-designed platform. Yes, a writer, for the
purposes of the moment. He would be a writer. It made
sense, because writers were oddly anonymous figures – or
so John supposed – quite lost in their task of examining the
unexamined lives.

It was possible – no, certain – that he'd got drunk the night
before. He definitely had a hangover when he awoke, fully
dressed, spread-eagled on his bed in the Graben Hotel;
awaiting a liver gnawing, although he had no recollection of
having stolen any fire the preceding evening. The phone on
the bedside table had rung; it was an anachronistic item,
cream Bakelite with an in-built radio. John had never seen
such a thing before now, before picking it up:

'Gross God!' barked a Wiener on the other end.

'Gross God.' John wearily intoned.

'We were just wondering . . .'

'Yes?'

'Well . . . when you might be checking out?'

'Now.'

'Yes?'

'Yes, now, can you order a taxi for me?'

'To the airport?'

'Yes.'

Really John should have stayed on the line, kept within the
confines of this helpful conversation. He might have been
able to elicit more information: 'Who am I?'

'Your name is John.'

'What am I doing in Vienna?'

'You are here on business.'

'What is my business?' And so on until all doubts were
erased.

At the hotel the television had been on, silently whining. On-screen hotel had succeeded on-screen hotel: the Oberoi Palace in New Delhi, the Oriental in Bangkok, Raffles in Singapore . . . all served by CNN. John remembered being told by someone . . . acquaintance? Friend? Adjacent queue member . . . ? that Ted Turner – the network's owner – was a manic depressive, whose hyperactive periods beggared description; speed synergized with global communications. Mmm. John pushed his head up a bit. Alcohol made you stupid, as flatly incapacitated as if you'd been clubbed around the chops with a four-kilo endangered cod.

Two smeary, bleary Johns peered back at John from the two, slightly ajar, mirrored doors, of the two, overly solid wardrobes, which graced the leaden room with their leaden presences.

Over by the double doors – like some Oxford college, perhaps that's why spies had favoured the place – there was a grey pool of piss on the light blue carpet. John knew it to be piss without needing to go over and assay the stuff; it could hardly be water. The toilet was next to the double doors, the bathroom nearer the made bed John was atop. It was hardly likely that he'd risen from the bed, gone to the honour bar (marvellous expression – honouring whom exactly?), fetched a tumbler, gone to the bathroom, poured himself a glass of water, walked to the main door and poured it on to the carpet. No way. Gross God.

The bit about the Oxford college was good – authentic, John thought, showed he knew his territory; not like Vienna, which despite its dinky, rococo elegance – or more likely because of it – was as undifferentiated as this cream.

John tasted a bit of the cream mound on his cappuccino. He felt the awkward companionship of his belly. A sculptor had once told John that what he feared most about growing old was that his sense of his body would become more and more extraneous, more hollow, until 'It'll be like your eyes are just two fucking holes cut in the outside, peep-holes in your own fucking body.' Had that been in Vienna, or London? The 'fucking' would imply that the man had been speaking English, but perhaps he hadn't said 'fucking' at all, it was all most puzzling. Perhaps the 'fucking' was a screen memory, utterly, suitably psychoanalytical for old Wien. Gross God.

It bit down on John that this was really the bitter essence of his middle years. He had, he knew this much, always fancied himself as a cynic when he was growing up, wise to the world's infinite modes of disappointment; so how could it be that the dark wood of the years closed in so on him now? The dark Vienna Woods. He really wouldn't have troubled being miserable all of those years if he'd known it was going to end up like this; with being both miserable and old. Drunkenness gave you an unnecessary taste for oblivion, for death.

A combined phone and radio actually made a good deal of sense. Obviously the first thing you thought about when you answered the telephone – given that it was on in the first place – was turning the radio off. Alternatively, once you'd put the receiver down, you might decide that you'd like someone else to talk to you, without the necessary labour of reply, and switch the radio on.

John had switched the radio on, risen shakily from the bed and made his way to the extravagantly net-curtained windows – three-metre billows of scratchy wispiness, full of cold, damp air from the street – but even on this small route things had felt wrong. He'd slept in his boots; dandified, suede ankle boots, not his usual style at all. And at the first pace he was aware of sweat sloshing in the toe, at the second the macerated mush of sock soaked by it, and at the third something intensely painful, an abrasive wire in the very cleft of his middle toes. Standing, stork-legged, visual field spattered with a holding pattern of spots, he got the boot off. John's toes were startled, white tubers, wrinkled at the top. At the mouth of the middle-toe cleft the skin was raised into a tight speckling of pink pimples. Dropping the boot, John leant down and parted the toes, sensing another grating wire of pain connect with his sore cortex. As he'd suspected, the skin was gone and the webbing was pitted with mini-bites, as if he'd been chomped on by three-millimetre-long rodents. It was a nasty little attack of athlete's foot. Damp micro-organisms gnawing at him in the mittel-European night.

What conceivably could have happened? John had a vision of himself being dragged along the dusky corridors of the Graben, his suede feet ploughing still darker furrows in the burgundy nap of the carpet, two burly Austrian athletes holding him up by respective armpits. Out front a black Merc' with tinted windows awaits, the driver smoking a toothpick-sized Dannemann. They chuck him in the back (Gerhard, a hammer-thrower, and Rolf, javelin; gifted amateurs, certain men of even temperament), drive to a gymnasium in Jedlesee, across the river. There they strip him in the changing rooms, drag him up and down the chequer-board of soiled tiles, liberally coating his naked feet in whatever infective matter may be circulating there, in amidst the dreck of water, toenail clippings, shed calluses, and worse. Then they stuff him back into his clothes and boots, throw him back in the Merc', drive him back across Reichsbrücke and dump him in his room back at the Graben.

How else could he have contracted athlete's foot (which was a fungus, wasn't it?), without ever undertaking exercise of any kind? Certainly, he hadn't the look of an athlete; although seen in the mirror, on the first of the mighty wardrobes, his figure was stocky enough. His suit was a rust colour, the cloth a light weave. A naevus of creases had exploded in his groin.

He still had his jacket on as well, and his red tie was yanked round to the side of his neck – perhaps there'd been an attempted lynching as well? But most surprising were the close-clipped – but full-curled – grey beard; and the corresponding helmet of contained, steely luxuriance. His eyes – blue irises, red whites, sag bags – peered out through fleshy goggles. His nose was a nosepiece; his ears irrelevant.

But John didn't feel bearded, not psychically. He'd run a stubby paw around his face, stroking the twisted pile of the thing. Strange. He took in the suit as well – its colour and cut. Neither seemed quite right – like the boots. The unusual radio-phone combinatorial device had eased its way back into John's narrative at this juncture; insinuating an American announcer with an Austrian accent – or perhaps the reverse: 'It's ten thirty-nine on the eighth of October, and here's the latest news from Radio Blue Danube. Presidential aides are continuing to . . .' then quit it again. Leaving behind only John's bemused sense of the faint absurdity of radio waves emanating from the Blue Danube, and the time.

He then launched a search for an air ticket – that's what the time check induced in him. A launch for an air ticket that might be his. Why else the request for a taxi to the airport – if it wasn't to catch a flight? He saw a wad of paper protruding from under the wardrobe to the right; 'Heavy 2' John had already christened it. This wad could've been there to keep the weighty furniture level, but when he withdrew it, John saw that it was indeed an air ticket: an oblong folder of stapled card, containing a tissue admission voucher to another landscape. He scanned the information – it was a Lufthansa flight, from Vienna to Frankfurt, departing at . . .

Shit! In an hour and fifteen minutes.

The peculiar dance of the late hotel guest – how funny to witness, how terrible to endure. St Vitus jigs from bathroom to wardrobe, to honour bar and back again. He plucks garments off hangers, whips them into bags; dumps toiletries into littler bags and whips them in as well. He stacks flat things in a briefcase – laptop, books, papers, receipts – and zips it bulbous. He counts the piddling miniatures in the wastebasket – the ones that made him piddle; and annotates the carbon-backed bill accordingly.

All this turbulence while John checked labels inside collars and the headings on letters. He glanced at the titles of books and peered within himself for any obvious referents. The name 'John' was on the air ticket in the ruled box denoting 'passenger', but was it a first or a last name? He could not have said, for his vision was smeared when it came to detail, as if spots of grease had coated the inside of his eyes. The personal effects and clothing were just that: elements of an identity that he felt quite certain he might either assume or reject at will. When it came to re-examining himself in the full-length mirror, prior to running the gauntlet of the lobby, John quite self-consciously noted that the creases in the suit were fading. The creases in this drip-dry, ersatz, quintessentially Central European suit.

John had looked more closely at the unslept-in bed than he did at any other thing in the room. Indeed, despite the feverish packing, he'd had plenty of time to dwell on its rucked counterpane and partially depressed pillows. Hadn't bed once been a refuge? He thought.

Hadn't he once looked towards bed as the most ineffable repose? Hadn't it been possible to pull at the downy edge of darkness and yank it over his cold body, drag it into cosiness? Why could he not forget the flight, the air ticket, the trade show in Frankfurt? Why not turn in and cheat the hangover of its grim dialectic?

It was not possible. Even as he packed the Janus-faced possessions into their conventional housings, John sensed that bed would for ever be an alien nation to him now.

That all beds would be like that of Room 25 in the Graben Hotel – Great Beds of Wear, of terminal uncosiness. He'd deftly combed his beard – how could that be? Did all men know instinctively how to comb beards; the psychic beards that, since adolescence, had lingered about their pale faces? Outside it was drizzling, cold. John looked in Heavy 1 and found a long, dark grey overcoat, with a synthetic, blue fur collar. He put it on – it fitted. Even so, not liking the feel of it, or the weight, or the way it flared in an effete fashion from the hips, he'd decided to look in Heavy 2 as well.

The mirrored door to Heavy 2 was jammed shut, jammed shut on a softish thing which prevented it being either opened or closed, so that it remained only a few centimetres ajar. How so? John had begun by gently prising it – the phrase 'bend but don't break' had come to him unbidden – but he

was in a hurry and there was a dreadfulness about the
jammed door which caused him to wrench hard on the
handle until the entire thing shifted with a double thud. There
was, John had concluded, something heavy inside Heavy 2;
something that was jamming the door. What could he do?
There was already the dishonoured bar and the piss pool,
could he explain this to the Manager of the Graben as well?
'Biegen aber nicht brechen.'

The telephone-radio had rung again at this point. 'Herr
Incomprehensible?'

'Yes?'

'Your cab is here.'

'I'm on my way.' And he had been. On his way to more
unpleasantness.

This time it was Mozart's *Requiem*. Astonishing how these
mobile-phone technicians could compress the full majesty of
a requiem mass into a few discordant bleeps and peeps.
There was no need any more for orchestras and opera halls;
Schwarzkopfs and von Karajans. Gross God. John looked
down to find that the cumuli of whipped cream had been
demolished with unconscious lightning strikes of his own
spoon. The gross god was angry. Now he simply had a slop
of average cloudiness.

In the taxi – which was not as long as a stretch, but neither
as short as a conventional Merc' – John had recovered some
of his composure. The quitting of the Graben had proved
both less and more traumatic than he'd feared. There was
one plum-blazered managerial type and a hovering porter
in a shortie white jacket. The lobby was fusty with rubber
plants, yuccas, leather chairs, wood panelling. Herr
Incomprehensible's bill had, it appeared, been settled.
Saving, naturally, charges for *telefon* and minibar. These John
had paid for with a swatch of schillings trawled from the suit's
pocket. Then a flurry of '*auf wiederschein*'s to the manager
and he and the bags and the porter were in the chill little
canyon of Dorotheergasse. Another flurry of valediction, the

porter palmed more notes and John plopped on to the upholstery. The porter ducked and *danke*-ed, winked conspiratorially, and whispered through the open window, 'I will look after your friend.'

Disconcertingly, the driver had chosen to back all the way up Dorotheergasse, his arm braced around the front passenger seat's headrest, his large, Wiener countenance confronting John's own. 'I think,' the driver had begun ponderously, as if he were about to enunciate an epoch-making, philosophical proposition, 'that they did not build these streets with cars in mind.'

'No, indeed,' John had muttered in reply, looking over the driver's shoulder at a retreating sliver of the Rotenturm. It was then that he had had an idea. Why not, in the spirit of the espionage role he seemed to have assumed, take back bearings on his own past, and thus establish his identity? Look at the retreating street of short-term memory. It was then that the absurd character of Vienna had impinged; then that the stuff about childhood and wieners had boiled up to the murky surface. Then that John had felt quite safe in his Englishness.

RED ZAC . . . BUDAPEST . . . W+3473ZE . . . SCHWECHAI . . . HASS . . . FLUGHAFEN 4KM . . .

Letters and figures whipped by the wings of the Merc' as it breasted the spray. Once he was out of the centre, the driver had pushed on relentlessly, imbuing the big saloon with so much inertia that it had felt as if they were falling. Taking front bearings, John realized, peering between the oblique gun sights on the bonnet was useless. Frankfurt was conceivable only as the most sketchy lineaments, washed-out stacks of children's plastic bricks: the towers of Mainhattan; and an exhibition hall as large as a despot's mausoleum, wherein rubber-wheeled electric carts ferry the trade delegates about. Entirely implausible.

But back bearings were another matter. The shops along the Ring glowing in the twilight. Blind people with white sticks singing Strauss Lieder from Braille music sheets. The smell of

coffee and cakes, followed abruptly by the sight of
middle-aged women eating them, their well-upholstered
bodies sat in well-upholstered chairs. Lace everywhere.
Gross God! It was overweening Wien! John saw his trouser
legs in a darkened doorway, a searchlight flirting with them.
He heard the synthesized strumming and plucking of a zither.
You could bottle these memories and sell them commercially.
Vienna was just this abstraction of elements; this decoction of
its own past; this world-beating lie. No wonder it felt so
suspiciously familiar – John, like anyone else of his age,
reared on Hollywood, could choose any number of travestied
cities within which to situate his ill-remembered past.

It had helped that the Merc' had felt as if it were falling.
Helped to place John's viewpoint some metres above his
dimly remembered past. There he was, walking beside a far
taller man, a man wearing a formal, dark overcoat,
unbuttoned over a severely cut, darker suit. The man was
gesturing at the blind choir, the shops and cafés, the
promenade full of hurrying Wieners. Evidently he had been
showing John around the old town, and presumably it had
been to him that John had retailed his anecdote.

It had. There was an appropriately filmic dissolve as the
pipeline galleries of an oil refinery strobed away to either side,
like the giant markers on a dial. An old Viennese apartment
resolved itself, and within it, seated around an oval table, six,
mismatched guests – four men, two women. The faces of the
other four were obscure, but John in his role as cornice-cam,
spotted his own hairy helmet and the tall man's slash of
profile, vis-à-vis across the table. Which had come first,
language or consciousness? It's impossible to imagine
thinking without language, but equally, can you speak without
ever thinking about it? And by the same token, is it possible
to have a character without having an identity?

Yet John's character must be perfused with the most
gaseous of ironies. Why else lean across the table, replete
with its sculpted serviettes, modelled entrées and arranged
flowers (clearly they had yet to begin), and say to the

assembled company: 'I'm just going to get a Vienna and
some chips . . .'? As if expecting a dry rustle of arid
acquiescence. What a wally. Gross God! Had this been said
in English or German? And what kind of response had he
possibly expected from this lot? This quintet of Wieners, in
amongst their Biedermeier effects. Certainly not what had
then occurred.

From his aerial perspective John saw five hands travel to
five throats and fiddle there. Five hands come away with five
sticks atop which were five faces – or rather masks. The
swine had taken their faces off – this *was* a masque. They
twirled them in the candlelight, revealing first the crumpled
expressions of strained civility, then nothing. At the side of the
room stood a glass cabinet full of ancient votary statues, oil
lamps and other, gently rocking bibelots.

The driver was looking at John in the rear-view mirror, an
expression of strained civility on his face. They were
sweeping around a spiral tongue of roadway. 'So, Brazil,
which airline would that be?'

'Brazil? Oh, yeah, right – No, no, Frankfurt, I'm going to
Frankfurt –'

'Right, Brazil was your little joke. Which airline for Frankfurt
then?'

'Lufthansa.'

A very little joke. An infinitesimal joke; a photon of hilarity
disappearing from the space–time continuum before it could
even be measured. John had paid the driver, assumed the
bags, marched off through the electronic doors. Going . . .
going . . . gone out of Vienna into international space. Or
so he had hoped as he set off with an efficient lope across
the shiny floor, a lope which soon slowed to a crimped
crawl. The athlete's foot – for this there was no international
rescue; and the hangover, back now with confident
bombast: a roll of kettledrums in the belly, five cor anglais in
his chest, and a triangle on the brain. He found his sick self
wandering amidst parades, displaying the same underwear.
And the glass cases full of Mont Blanc pens, and the cases

full of camcorders, and the aisle upon aisle of tiny dirndls.

Gurgling out of John had gone the irony and the playfulness. The neat, shiny pretzel had been the residuum of this. Yet still he struggled on with the back bearings, struggled to bring the wavering beam of the searchlight from shoes, to trouser cuffs, to overcoat, to face. The glass cases of goods were rearrangements of the products that were on display in the city. Different room – same things. It reminded him of the way that Freud's effects had been packed up in 1938 and transposed over to London, where they'd been placed in approximately the same positions, in the front room of another comfortable home. The cabinets full of Freud's myriad of miniature antiquaries; the ottoman-blanketed chaise-longue; the bookcases full of the canon. But had he seen these things in London . . . or Vienna, where – Gross God! – they had a plenty big enough Freud Museum.

Leaving the aisle of tiny dirndls, he'd seen immigration and customs dead ahead, together with a row of automated check-in points. Why not? But once he'd gone through, traversed another esplanade of shops, gone down an escalator, up another, he'd found himself back where he'd begun – still 'land side' – and temporarily given up. Berthed himself in this café – was it a subsection of the airport, or was the airport an extension of it? – and ordered the aforementioned cappuccino; listened to the extempore songs of the mobile phones.

It was the childhood anecdote, the one about the wieners, that had accelerated the pace of the evening. It was after this that the masks had come off. Why had he told it?

Why had he been unable to judge the effect that this would have on Herr Direktor, Frau Direktor and the others? Until then it had been – how would you say it? I don't know – swimming between them. But afterwards, after the obligatory sluice of wine had washed them back into the streets, they'd ceased waving and begun to drown in each other's contempt. Why had he behaved in this fashion? He was a writer – true enough, but that gave him no licence. He was

here as a representative of his country – like any other. Did he
not realize the importance of these people?

They had reeled along together, the tall Englishman and
the stocky Austrian. The quiff of brown hair bobbed beside
the helmet of grey. There had been a bar, then another, then
a third. At one point they found themselves in front of the
carious calcifications of the cathedral, and he'd pointed out
the secret sign of the resistance, figures scratched on an
archway. The other had laughed, saying that the two
numbers indicated the size of the resistance, not its
intentions. Once started – he wouldn't stop. It'd all come up.
Kurt Waldheim, Thomas Bernhard – whatever. He'd gestured
around him in the empty square, almost shouting: 'And
where are they?! Where?!' Then singing, in a grotesque pop
parody: 'Where've all the Hutus gone, lo-ong time ago!', then
rounded on him, shoved his sharp nose at him and slurred,
'Well, where've they gone? Y'don't see many Hutus sitting
down at the pavement cafés of Old Kigali, now doo-yoo?
This place is full of fucking gho-osts!' Then pirouetted away, a
madman in an overcoat: 'Oh – Vi-enn-aaaa!'

At the Graben they'd attempted to patch things up over
two Johnny Walker reds, two Jack Daniels, two Gordon's
gins, two Stolichnayas and eventually, belatedly, two
Underbergs.

They'd talked of Ted Turner's mania and the dark woods of
middle age. They'd discussed their bodies and how time had
winnowed them out, left them hollow, looking through slits for
eyes. And by dawn they'd reached some kind of concord; at
any rate there was silence from within the wardrobe. Heavy 2.

He stood, and looking around him at the precincts of the
airport, felt once again the dawn of the European Union of
Facelessness. He called for the bill, and while it was added
and brought, the loose garment of his assumed identity
began to fall from his shoulders, until he was an Austrian in a
rust-coloured suit, with a red tie. An Austrian in a fur-collared,
Austrian overcoat. He would have to go back to the Graben –
what could he have been thinking? The false check-out and

still falser check-in, could only work for a matter of hours. *Biegen aber nicht brechen*. He would have to look inside Heavy 2. Have to find out if the porter really had looked after his 'friend'. His friend, to whom Vienna had seemed so absurd.

What a wally.

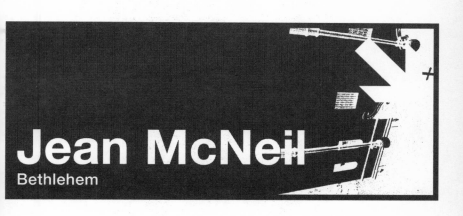

Jean McNeil

Bethlehem

Jean McNeil is from Canada, but in
1991 she fled to London, where she
has lived since, apart from long periods
spent in Brazil, Mexico and Central
America. Her novel, Hunting Down
Home, was published in the UK and
Canada in 1996, where it was
shortlisted for the Commonwealth Prize
(Canada and the Caribbean), and is
forthcoming in the US in 1999. She is
also the author of the Rough Guide to
Costa Rica, and an author of the

Rough Guide to Central America.

She is running back and forth to the bathroom, getting towels
to put underneath him. The boy sits on the edge of the bed.

'I'm not gay, Señora.'

'That's reassuring,' she says in English.

The boy scowls. '*Qué?*'

She switches to Portuguese. 'He's my husband.'

'Sure.' The boy shrugs. He can see she wears no ring.

Behind the boy his hands are tied to the bedstead in a
loose noose. They rotate gently within the confines of the
rope, which has been covered in strips of pillowcase.

She disappears into the tiny bathroom. When she emerges
she is carrying a towel. She wrings her hands in it first,
noticing a dark brown ring underneath her nails, next to the
skin – dried blood. Suddenly her hands look alien, like
mandibles, or claws; the appendages of another species.

She flicks the wall switch, turns on the fan. 'I have to dress
his wound first.'

'What's wrong with him?'

The boy's copper skin has turned to onyx in the soupy
light. It is the rainy season and dark has fallen at four o'clock.
Peru-shaped clouds bloom, these rain-clouds that float
across the Amazon basin every afternoon.

She doesn't answer the boy. She concentrates on
dressing the wound, slapping on the yellow lotion and
winding the gauze around his midriff. He whispers something
in her ear, but she misses the sense of it. She kisses his
forehead. She does all this with the same detachment she
would feel if she were watching herself on film. Everything she
does seems to happen too slowly. Even the walls of the room
look very far away.

'I've been shot too, Señora.' He pulls up his shirt to show

her a tiny puckered scar just to the right of his abdomen.

'Good for you. Here, catch.' He claps his hands over the small packet. The boy opens his hands and grins. She leans against the wall. 'Put it on.'

As the boy unbuttons his jeans she goes to sit in the chair by the window. The sheer curtain floats in the breeze and brushes her hair like an insect. She watches them closely, noting all the manœuvres and sequences, as if she were cataloguing them. The only thing that still surprises her is how men can become aroused without really feeling any particular desire. Otherwise she is not shocked. It is really heterosexual sex she finds most disturbing; the appendages fitting each other with the puerile ease of Lego.

After a while the boy begins to moan.

'*Basta*,' she says. Enough.

She pulls him off the bed. She hates it when they moan – it sounds like the death cries of animals. She stuffs some cruzeiros into his hand. He scowls. He had been expecting dollars. He trips into his trousers, his graceless movements revealing his youth. He is all gangling adolescent limbs.

When he is in the hall she shuts the door behind him and turns to the man on the bed. He is sweating. She goes into the bathroom to get more towels to wipe him down. When she pulls on the light cord she cannot help seeing her face in the mirror. She grabs another of the too-thin towels and quickly pulls off the light.

I love to watch the rains come. It doesn't get dark so much as the sky seems to become coated with metal. Then it comes, bulleting and horizontal. Pot-holes open in the streets, as if they've always been there, like wounds underneath the skin of the asphalt, waiting to open.

About once a week after the rains I go to buy earrings in the market by the cathedral. I make a lot of friends in the market, because only tourists usually shop there and they speak little or no Portuguese. I have picked up the deep-throated, meowing accent of Pará. I even use the *tu* and conjugate it correctly. This is an interesting regionalism; nobody but people from Pará do this, in the whole of Brazil.

The Basilica de Nossa Señora de Nazaré is my favourite church in this city of heat-stunned churches. It is modelled upon St Paul's in Rome. Not far from our apartment building is the quarter where the rubber barons used to live. The best of these Portuguese mansions have been built, natives of Belém tell me, by Antônio Lemos and Lauro Sodré. Brazilians say their names with the gravity usually reserved for military heroes. It's one of the things I like most about this country – they hold their architects in reverence. The buildings are the colour of faded lime, oyster-hued, and peeling, as if they have been attacked by some kind of eczema. In the middle of a rainstorm the whole city looks like a torched Versailles, or the earthquake-smashed apartments of ancient Pompeii.

I go out so often that a lot of people know me on sight by now. There is not a large foreign community, so people are not exhausted and surly in the face of my inevitable foreignness. I could love this city, if I were here under different circumstances. I even take an interest in the riot scenes in the supermarkets, when shoppers discover rice has been made more expensive yet again. Inflation is running at 46 per cent a month. To a degree I am protected by my cache of American dollars. I don't know why he is indifferent to the city. He behaves like someone who has come here to die. He has become very interior, fixated upon himself and his reactions. As far as he is concerned, he could be in Calcutta, or Toronto. Maybe this is just his way of saying he wants to go home.

I love to watch the rains come but sometimes I wonder why I stay here. We're young: he's twenty-four, I'm twenty-one. We're almost out of money. We should go home, I should leave him. But I'm still edgy, still hungry for experience.

The nearest slum neighbourhood, *favela*, is where she goes to make her contacts for him.

Without Lourdes, she could not have dreamed of entering the *favela*. Lourdes has lissom legs, trim and pretty. She can see the girl takes great care with her appearance; her hair is always neatly clipped in pink plastic butterfly-shaped hair pins, her shirts always spotlessly white. Most days she wears the same pair of blue shorts, but every day they are pressed and clean. She manages to keep up this level of hygiene and meticulousness in a one-room tin shack where she, her father and half-brother live.

As she enters with Lourdes through the darkened house, shapes shift in the corners – people rising from the floor, or falling down; she can't tell which. They pass through the house and emerge through the back door into narrow alley-ways of corrugated tin-roof dark squares. As they descend the stairs to the alley-way Lourdes walks in front of her, putting each foot delicately on the mulch-soft wooden steps.

Then she sees him, or at least she thinks it's a he, judging from his bulk. He lies on his side, his head propped up by an arm. Folds of fat droop where his biceps should be. Lying on his platform, which has the slab-aspect of a masseur's table or a surgeon's bed, he looks like a whale or a beached seal. His mouth is lipsticked, his hair drawn back into a bun. He wears a purple piece of material, the exact colour of the açai berries that came from the jungle, which is draped over his flounderous body in the style of a toga. His dark skin glistens as if it has been greased. His eyes, she notices, are extremely cunning.

'Is he a man or a woman?' she asks Lourdes, when they are past him.

'Who? Gorda?' The girl grins, hiding her mouth behind her hand. 'Who knows? A man. We think.'

'Then why is he called Gorda, in the feminine, as you would call a woman?'

'I don't know.'

'Is he homosexual?'

Lourdes considers this for a few seconds. 'What do you mean?'

She gave her mock-severe look. 'You know very well what that means. Don't tell me you can live years in a place like this and not know. It means a man who likes men, or a woman who likes women.'

Lourdes screws up her face. 'Will you buy me an ice cream?'

'Sure,' she says, taking her by the hand. 'Let's go.'

'It's not really a zoo,' Lourdes corrects her, pointing to the sign – Bosque Rodrigo Alves. She has taken Lourdes there to buy her an ice cream. 'It's a Bosque. How do you say that in English?'

'Wood.'

Lourdes shifts her mouth in emulation of her consonants. 'Voooodd.'

'That's right. You've got it.'

'There are more animals at the Goeldi. Do you want me to take you there?'

'Sure, let's go.' She does not tell the girl she has been to the Emlio Goeldi museum at least five times already.

They enter the gardens, following a path of gravel the colour of woodchips. On either side of them are clumps of tropics vegetation. It is early morning and a weekday, so they almost have the place to themselves. She reminds herself that she must avoid the snakes, but they go up there anyway, she and Lourdes leaning over the railings, looking at the boa and the anaconda, which are kept in cages placed next to each other. The boa drapes itself over a bare, constructed tree branch like an exhausted innertube. The anaconda lolls in the water. They can only see its eyes and its massive head.

'Which do you think is bigger?' Lourdes' vanilla ice cream drips down her fingers. She exits her tongue, small and feline, to lap it up.

'I think the anaconda is the biggest snake in the world, so it must be bigger.'

Lourdes licks her ice cream thoughtfully. 'I like them.'

'I hate them.'

They move on to the alligators. 'These are imported

alligators,' Lourdes informs her officially. 'They were brought
here from Florida.'

'They should have only Amazonian animals here. It's not as
though there aren't enough of them, or that they don't need
protection.'

Lourdes looks at her sharply. She has to remind herself
that most Brazilians are unused to hearing opinions about the
United States that are not entirely positive.

They move on to the aviary, where the macaws are making
a racket. Lourdes has finished her ice cream and is looking
longingly at her soggy napkin, which has mopped up most of
the melted vanilla.

'There's one more thing you have to see before you go,'
Lourdes says, pulling at her arm. 'The Amazon is famous for
it. Do you know what it is?'

She smiles, shakes her head.

'Oh, come on.' Lourdes doubles her body up into a
burlesque of impatience. 'It's this big.' She throws her arms
out on either side of her body, her face turning pink with
strain.

'*Não,*' she shakes her head, trying not to laugh. '*Não
posso imaginar.*'

'The Victoria Régia lily. Do you know, this flower is like
Gorda. It is both male and female. It changes overnight.
That's why it's so big.' Lourdes begins to frown in
concentration. 'It begins the day as a male, but then, at dusk
it traps this insect, a beetle. And it uses this beetle to
pollinate –' Lourdes grinned, proud of her use of the word –
'to reproduce itself. And then, by morning, it has become a
female. The plant, not the beetle.'

'And does it let the beetle go in the morning?'

Lourdes frowned. 'I don't know.'

They go to the indoor exhibit, billed as 'The Natural History
of the Amazon'. 'Belém.' Lourdes points to the sign on one of
the bird displays that recounts the importance of the trade in
tropical birds to the city. 'I can read that word. Do you know
what it means? Bethlehem.' The girl stumbles over the

consonants, unable to aspirate the *h* and concretize the *t*, so
that it comes out sounding like Betchleheem.

'Bethlehem.'

Lourdes cracks up laughing. For the rest of the morning
she coaches the girl to say it properly, in English. Lourdes
insists. Still, she wonders if she had been cruel, teaching the
girl to say a word she will never use again.

At noon, they part.

'You have to get back to your *namorado*,' Lourdes states,
a little flatly. *Namorado* means both 'boyfriend' and 'betrothed'.

'Yes.'

'I know a good new boy for you, Ana,' Lourdes says, using
her name. She doesn't normally do this; she's doing it for the
same reason a salesman would, to pretend or invite familiarity.

Suddenly, she feels sullied. She wants to let the girl know
that their friendship can be pure.

'He's not for me.'

Lourdes says nothing, just walks away from her, turning to
look over her shoulder from time to time, but she keeps on
walking, without turning around, heading for home.

Lone taxis scoot up and down the wide streets that lead to
the docks like frightened rodents. Massive gutters are built
alongside each *rua* and *avenida* to trap the daily deluge. They
are so big, in any other city I'm sure they would be called
canals.

Every day, all year, it rains twice a day. Once at one
o'clock, once at five. The second instalment of rain is less
predictable. But the sky is almost always clear in time to see
the sun disappear into the river.

Our apartment is on the eleventh floor. We live in the
highest high-rise in Belém, on Praça Tiradentes
('Toothpuller's Plaza'). It is American in style, furnished in
chrome and mirrors, but Brazilian in intent. The kitchens all
have a maid's elevator leading on to them, and a small
maid's room, right next to the laundry room. For a Brazilian,
an apartment like this costs a fortune. But we have dollars.

Every evening at five-thirty I go out on to our balcony and watch the sunset. To the right are the docks – the oblong forms of warehouses look like greased lozenges in the setting sun. Cranes tower above them, lop-sided, delicate. In the distance is the Ilha do Marajó – a wedge of green dotted with what looks like lakes. This time of year the island is a virtual floodplain.

To the left is the river, heading toward its intersection with the Xingú. And to the north, nothing, at least for us city dwellers. Only an untraversible forest stretching from here to the Guyanas. For most of the foreigners and the wealthy Brazilians, the only thing north of Belém of any significance is Miami. Both Varig and VASP have daily flights there. I see them taking off from the airport, which is also visible from my balcony. Planes are so different when they fly in; they seem to come in at half-speed, hovering like exhausted metal angels. When they take off they are as clear and intentful as an arrow; they almost seem to write MIAMI OR BUST.

One or two nights a week we go out to eat. We always end up in one of the many very good seafood restaurants.

'We should stop eating so much shrimp.' He makes a face, as soon as we have ordered shrimp again. 'I never thought I'd be sick of shrimp.'

I like vatapá, a shrimp dish in a rich sauce made from Amazonian fruit. But my favourite is maniçoba, meat cooked in leaves from the bitter casava, which are also toxic, at least under most circumstances. To be used in cooking, its leaves first have to be simmered for a full eight days, to drain them of their natural poison.

She opens the door to their apartment. As soon as she opens it she feels a wave of tiredness wash over her. The plants look plastic, she notes, for the hundredth time. Even though they are real. Then, that's the tropics.

He sits watching a telenovella to improve his Portuguese – its name translates into 'As the World Turns'.

'Hi,' he grins, and turns his eyes upon her.

She has seen his eyes hundreds of times before, but she
will never exhaust their magnificence. They are dark green,
not large, but perfectly framed by thick ginger eyelashes.
Chapped skin flakes off around his straight nose and thin,
svelte eyebrows. His lips are full, criss-crossed-crossed like
the stitching in a quilt. His hair is red-gold, he has a
prominent but not jutting jaw line, and wide-sprung
cheekbones showing traces of a Slavic ancestry. His face, as
always, causes her to think of unlikely foreign phenomena,
the loping walk of the Bushmen of the Kalahari, of the
disdainful turned-down mouths of the ancient Incas. Every
time she looked at him she felt a kind of exquisite shifting
taking place inside her, as if she were made up not of veins
and organs but sand bars.

He is not a large man, but his limbs are perfectly in
proportion. He is still almost as muscled as he was when he
went to the gym every day. She has never seen anyone, not
even Lourdes, who has such beautiful limbs. His forearms, for
instance, which are tendon-hard, and are intersected by a
riverine network of veins. Sometimes she runs her forefinger
along them, pointing to the places where they branch.

'That's the Tapajós,' she says, where one thick vein
departs from another. 'That's the Solimoẽs.'

His skin has the delicacy of parchment. She can swing
next to him in a hammock and not say anything for hours.
They don't need to talk. But she doesn't like the burnt-metal
taste of this supposed languor, this relatively cheap idyll.

She's aware that this is not real life, even though she
enjoys her friends and her life, her students. She loves the
city. Even in the midst of her experience of living there, she
already knows she will never forget it. But she also knows it is
a place to be left behind in favour of more rigorous realities.
He does not seem to realize this. Sometimes she thinks he
has no aspirations in particular.

Later, they sit together in the darkness in front of the
window, illuminated by the sodium light of the docks. Flecks
of white dot the river – the headlamps of boats. On the

inky river they seem to form a mirrored pattern of the stars.

'You are everything to me.'

Does she say this, or does she just think it?

From the moment she met him – when she had to lean against the wall for support, such was the impact of seeing someone for whom she'd been waiting – she had never expected not to know, at any point, where he was; whether he lived or died.

Sometimes she has this vision of him out in the world, without her. He is in Srinagar, maybe, the hue of his beautiful ochre skin the exact colour of deserts waiting for the rains to come. He has the grace that all people whose fingers are longer than their palms share. In his every movement is the same fluidity as that of a lazy swimmer, heavy with supper, about to go under.

Between her fingers is his hair. It feels as soft as the tendrils of sea anemones. Noises from the docks, twenty blocks away, crackle into the apartment. Eleven storeys up, she thinks, you hear everything.

Night falls. On the equator, she has the impression that the world does not turn.

When they left behind the northern winter and came to Brazil she thought she would hear sounds of dense forests at night. She wanted to be surrounded by a breathing, whispering conspiracy of trees. But it was the sounds of the city that came to her every night – Rio de Janeiro, Salvador, São Paulo, Manaus, and finally Belém. She could only make money teaching English in the cities.

When they first came to the Amazon they flew in from Brasilia. In the plane, she saw Manaus rise up beneath them like a giant satellite dish. Fifty feet from the edge of the airport runway was the rainforest.

A few days later they flew to Belém. The plane took off just before dusk. From her window seat she watched the night come over the river. They flew into its mouth in increasing darkness; to her left, towards Venezuela, the sky was streaked purple. Then she lost the shape of the river beneath her in the night.

That night in their hotel in Belém, he took a wisp of her hair in his hand, twirled it between his fingers.

'It's not you I need.'

'Who is it,' she said. '*Who?*'

She thought she was shouting, her voice came out a whisper. In that way it was like a dream.

'*What –*' he said. His lips were dry and they smacked as he said it, the sound of desert-bleached bones brushed by wind. ' *– what I need.*'

That night she went out on her own, into the still-baking thoroughfares, clogged with vehicles whose axles and undercarriages were caked with red dirt from driving the Trans-Amazonica highway. Curtains of rain brushed her cheek. Steam rose from her linen and cotton clothes, once crisp, now soaked as sex-soiled sheets.

From our balcony eleven floors above the city I can see the ferry to Macapá wandering into the river. I've never been there and from what I've heard I don't want to go. It is a heat-ragged city on the northern rim of the Amazon with a soccer field, a landing dock, and not much else. I've seen the ferry leaving the dock, barely moving as it slogs through the muddy river. It's an old rusting tub by any standard, so it won't have any navigational equipment. By some sonar instinct – like bats – it dodges the hulks of big cargo boats, the Amazon steamers. The boat from Belém leaves at midnight and takes twenty-six hours to cross the Amazon. That means it arrives at two in the morning. The transport schedules in the Amazon are unreal: buses leave at three or four in the morning and arrive at the same time. No wonder no one gets any sleep.

Caracas is a four-hour flight away. The cities which are near, at least in relative terms – Cayenne, Manaus – are still jungle backwaters. Even Lima or Bogotá is five hours' flying time away, including the inevitable stops in Letícia. Rio and

São Paulo are about five hours by air, in the frigid south. Only
the very rich of Belém go there with any frequency. Everyone
else takes the bus to Brasilia, if they really have to. That takes
two and a half days. New York is an impossibility, Paris so
remote as to not exist at all. Although I still hear people talk
about it occasionally, in the tone usually reserved for
speaking of jewels, or jaguar pelts, or other endangered or
near-destroyed objects – *Paris*.

Instead of the Seine and its bulb-garlanded tourist boats I
have the açai-berry boats landing at eleven-thirty each night.
The berries are brought to Belém from all over the mouth of
the Amazon. Some evenings I watch them come in to their
docks below the Círculo Militar, the army-fortress compound.
They look like migrating eels, long thin boats, their cyclops
eyes piercing the night like fireflies. When the boats land,
small, dark men scuttle to unload the heaps of fruit.

Açai – I love the name, its medicinal, swishy sound. I like
the taste even more, even though on their own the purple
berries are far too sour. They can be mashed with sugar and
mixed with maníoc, to make a purple couscous. More often
though, they are sugared and used to make ice cream the
colour of virulent bruises.

At these moments I don't feel I occupy a periphery,
somewhere dreamed of only by centuries of scientists and
merchants and other alarmists but forgotten by everyone
else. I feel I am at the fulcrum of the universe. Nowhere on
earth is as flat and broad and significant as this part of
Amazonia. All along the two-thousand-kilometre length of the
river, the elevation barely rises two hundred metres. I really
believe those National Geographic sentences, the ones that
tell me I am living in the lungs of the world.

They are having breakfast. As always, he seems nervous
when he eats, trembling, plucking at his napkin as if it were a
chicken that needed to be defeathered.

'The newspapers in the Amazon are such crap.' He points
to the corner of the table, where one of the body-count

papers that dedicated itself to corpses and accidents lies in a frustrated heap.

'You knew that before we came here. Why don't you go out and buy the *Folha de São Paulo*?'

'Because my Portuguese isn't as good as yours. I can only look at blood and guts pictures.'

'I'll translate for you.'

'No thanks. I'm dependent on you for enough already.'

'You'd rather complain.'

'I would.' He smiled. 'Oh, God,' he groans. 'Another story about the damage anthropologists are wreaking. This is a great joke,' he grins. 'What's a typical Kayapó family? A mother, a father, five kids and an anthropologist.'

She moans and rolls her eyes.

'Why don't we go to Salinópolis this weekend?' he says. 'I want to go to the beach.'

'I don't think we can.'

'You mean we can't even afford that? A weekend in Salinópolis, the Daytona Beach of the north-east?'

'This apartment costs a lot. You know that.'

'So,' he shrugs. 'Let's move.'

'We can't.'

'Why not?'

She pauses, looked down at her hands. 'I need the view.'

We can't afford to go to Salinópolis on the Atlantic so we go to Icoaraçi, a good river beach only half an hour by bus out of town. For a river beach, it's OK. There are not many piranha, almost no chance of bilharzia – the water is too swift-moving. There are crocodiles, though.

The beach is crowded on the weekends with Amazonian families and their children, who glisten like lizards. The fresh water seems heavy and sticks to my skin like mercury. We drink chilled coconut milk, he meets sylph boys at beach bars. In the distance I can see the low flat shape of an island. I wonder where the crocodiles are.

*

'I have to go out.'

He eyes her. 'OK.'

'Do you want me to bring anyone back?'

'No.' He shakes his head far more emphatically than he has done in a long time, except during sex. 'Just go out and enjoy yourself.'

He hardly goes out now. On the nights when he used to accompany her ventures into the city, they would sit in the Bar do Forte, built on the battlements of the old *fortaleza*, the one that overlooks the Ver-O-Peso market. The *fortaleza* once defended the entire Amazon against the English and the Dutch.

From there they used to watch ships sliding like giant glass structures over the Amazon. At night the river and sky are a seamless horizon of black, occasionally sequinned by the lights of the massive dock cranes, which warp and wink like the eyes of dinosaurs. Some nights they would go on to the Clube Lapinha, which she knew Belém natives avoided. Tourists are always fascinated by it because there are toilets for three sexes: Men, Women and Gay.

Now she has become so used to being alone in the city that she finds his presence obtrusive. Other men never looked at her in the street when he was with her. She is treated deferentially in bars and restaurants. She knows why – with him she is a Señora, an attached woman. Historically, women's survival in the Amazon depended upon having the protection of a man, she knew. Either that or they could become prostitutes.

Most of the time he stayed in their apartment, reading classics on their eleventh-floor balcony. She would come home to find him in the chair, sometimes asleep, with Ovid and Aeschylus and Plato and Cavafy sitting at his feet like puppies.

She missed seeing him in action, out in the world, because his being was calibrated on the cusp of action-obsessiveness and languor, and she knew this was unusual. When he did things, even if it were just buying fish at the Ver-O-Peso, he

did so decisively, and with a need that was ragged, intense
and controlled at once. He kissed her like that, too, but there
was also a languor in his limbs and lips. He let them linger on
hers until something inside her became insupportable. If she
could X-ray him and see his innards she was sure she would
see something that was in the process of melting. That's how
he felt when he touched her: frozen maple syrup or chilled
chocolate warming up, returning to its natural viscosity.

When she enters the air-conditioned office that afternoon, the
one that pays her meagre salary, or into a travel agency to
investigate flights they cannot afford, her body breathes a
sigh of relief. Her business done, she goes back into the
cracked pavements, insane carapaces driven by rain and rot,
into the shoe stores tumbling on to the street.

The Organization of American States is in town. Heat-
stunned gringos wander the broken pavements, avoiding
crevasses, stepping delicately, like storks. All the minor
statesmen and their acolyte bureaucrats have convened on
the city for six days. She tries to avoid the North Americans,
their pale and fleshy faces remind her too much of what she
is, herself. Still, just for a moment, she wants to go home.

The nights have got worse, not better, since they came to
Belém. Most nights now he has to uncurl her from her
screwdriver sleep postures. In the middle of the night all her
muscles contract, as if she were a stroke victim, and she
doubles up upon herself. He prises the pillow out of her
hands. He sits at her thighs. The *click-click* sound of the
docks filters in through the window. Light from the halogen
floodlights used to illuminate the night-time loading makes its
way in, too, bathing them in a sick hospital yellow.

He sinks down on one elbow and swings his legs up on
the bed. All this time he says nothing, but begins to stroke
her hair, moving it off her forehead. Then he lays himself out
against her and straightens her out, limb by limb, like a store
mannequin.

From time to time she would picture herself, or at least try to, with someone else – someone who returned her love at its exact pitch and frequency. Then she would replay their conversations. Every time she talked to him, she felt she was going somewhere she had never been before. No one else had ever given her that sense of possibility, and she clung to it even while she understood that its promise was false in the way that a journey undertaken in a dream does not really get you anywhere, at least not when judged by the moment of waking.

Although he is in a way every inch the Western man, his smooth limbs and chiselled face suggesting infinite progression, she can tell he is becoming increasingly dark, interior. Just talking to him is like entering an abandoned labyrinth. He often takes off his glasses to look at her, and even in the moment she would wonder if this was a calculated move of his, as if he knew the effect of the jade-threaded clarity of his eyes.

Still, she can't imagine he has any need to manipulate her. They can sit together happily for hours on the couch, facing the window of their apartment, their fingers twining and untwining. She runs her fingers through his hair, rubs the point on his neck where his hair stops and his skin begins. Her body flushes hot, just from this activity. If he falls asleep beside her, their thighs running alongside each other, she fingers his eyelashes, very lightly. They are extraordinarily long, like a camel's. She runs her finger through the whorls in his ear. She can do this for hours and not be ware of time passing. Then she might look up, suddenly, and see that outside the sky has turned to aluminium. Rain's coming.

The OAS conference brought opportunistic traders from all over the mouth of the Amazon. After she encountered a glut of Canadians, she walked down to the Ver-O-Peso. Under a massive Amazonian sky, pelicans fell like bombs into the brown waters. Or they waited opportunistically with the hunch-shouldered posture of diplomats next to the fish stalls. Some of the pelicans were as tall as the women who mind

the tattered stalls. The late-afternoon light was silk-washed.
The sun would go down in less than an hour.

'Señora, Señora.'

She turned around to see a man, his face creased with the
lines of too many false smiles. His forehead wide, his hair cut
by some maniac. She could see immediately that he was a
caboclo – of mixed indigenous and Portuguese blood. He
wore a brown-stained white sleeveless shirt and blue nylon
shorts. On his feet were flip-flops.

'I have something show you,' he said, in burring English,
and winked at her.

'*Que?*' She pretended not to understand.

He switched to Portuguese.

'*Vem conmigo.*'

She did not know why, but she went with him. It was not a
safe face, but she went with him anyway.

He turned his back to her, bent down, and reached into a
box, carefully, all the while whispering, '*Mínha amor, mínha
amor.*'

From the box he pulled what looked to be an animal.

She stood back. The first thing she noticed was the smell –
like rotting leaves. The animal's fur was grey and wiry and
was covered with what looked to be a dark green slime.

The animal faced the man, gripping his shoulders with two
short arms. Then it rotated its head, very slowly, and turned
to look at her. Its eyes were the colour of black licorice
streaked with amber. Its stare was inquisitive, and sad.

'Don't cry, Señora. Here, she's yours.'

She approached the animal. Its nose was squashed,
button-like. Over its eyes was a band of dark hair, like a
racoon's mask. She realized its benevolent expression came
from its upturned mouth; two thin black lips, smiling.

'Only thirty dollars, Dona.'

She took it in her arms. The animal gripped her shoulders
with its claws. She was made nearly delirious by the heat and
damp coming from its body.

She turned to the man, smiling. 'She's beautiful.'

The sloth gripped her just like a child, each leg splayed on her hip bones, its claws snug but not biting on her shoulders. It seemed to move very slowly, like a computer-generated animal.

She could hear the *thump-thump* of its heart. It was very slow. The sloth had extremely long claws. She feels her skin being serrated, but the sloth does not puncture it.

She looked into its face but wasn't sure what it was she could see there. Its nose touched her forehead, it was hot and wet. The sloth put its nose in her ear and she flinched, then smiled.

'She's trying to tell you something,' the man grinned. Then he pried the sloth off her body.

'Thirty dollars, Señora.' He put the animal back in the box.

'Wait here.' She thrust fifteen dollars into his hands. 'That's a deposit. I'll be back this afternoon.'

She wanders in and out of the afternoon rainstorms, going nowhere. She stands beneath their waterfall wetness, emerging from time to time into curtains of sunshine.

Near dusk she finds herself in Lourdes' neighbourhood. She can't remember going there. She has no appointment to meet her. He doesn't need a boy tonight.

The undergrowth of the house and into the courtyard of neatly arranged tin shacks. As she descends the stairs she expects to see him there on his slum divan. But Gorda is not there today.

She arrives at Lourdes' shack and, as there is no door, steps into the gloom. She steps back, blinks a couple of times, re-enters. By this time the girl has lowered the gun and holds it limp, at her thigh. She blinks again. It is unmistakably Lourdes. She looks just as she has always looked – a young girl, long-legged and intelligent.

'What are you doing with that?'

The girl shrugs. The gun falls out of her hand, thumps to the dirt floor.

'That's loaded. You never, *ever*' – she stepped forward to take Lourdes' face in her hands – 'You never,' she nearly squeals, her voice still constricted, 'let a loaded gun drop on the ground, do you hear me?'

Lourdes doesn't look at her.

'If you load a gun then you use it. You point it at someone and you use it.' She is shouting now. She is shaking the girl by her shoulders. 'Who were you going to shoot?'

The girl goes limp as a mollusc, comes to her, slides against her body.

'Oh, Ana . . .'

She has to remember that this is not her real name, only what she told Lourdes she was called. She feels guilty, suddenly, that this girl who trusts her thinks her name is something that it is not.

The girl puts her arms around her chest. Her flat body pinches itself against her breasts. She takes Lourdes' oblong face between her hands.

'Who were you going to shoot?'

Lourdes lowers her eyes.

'Who?' She shakes her.

'I don't know.'

She felt sad, immediately, as soon as the girl had said it. She didn't need to know who Lourdes had intended to shoot. She didn't need to ask that question. Later that night, as they lay entwined together, listening to the fizz of rain on the tin roof, Lourdes stirs, turns to her, only a shard of her face visible in the moon's knife coming through the window.

'Will you do something for me?'

She fans the girl's eyelashes between her index and third fingers. Lourdes closes her eyes.

'I'd do anything for you.'

She unbuttons her shirt and reaches both arms to her back, unclasps her bra. She releases her arms and lets her breasts strew out. Lourdes moves her mouth towards the nipple, closes over it.

On her breast the mouth is delicate, unscarred. It does not feel like a child suckling her breast. But it feels very different from when he does it. He does not close his mouth over her nipple, softly, but devours it, seems to want to swallow it. Lourdes stays like that for what seems like hours, until she falls asleep with the nipple in her mouth. For the first time since she met him, she sleeps with her body relaxed. No one has to come in the night and pry her apart. About an hour later, after the rain has stopped, she gently extricates her breast from the girl's open mouth, picks up the gun from where it had fallen, and leaves.

Much later that night she sits in the Tip-Top ice cream parlour, licking her favourite flavour, the bitter-lemony cupuaçú. Families take desultory promenades around the square to the rattling sound of axle-battered cars, combatants of too many Belém pot-holes. The sky is clear, but it is a sideways, neon night.

In the park women are arguing with their boyfriends. The women always take the initiative in an argument, she observes. The men are pliant, as if drugged. They go along with everything until they start drinking.

She has only a thousand cruzeiros left. Not much. She has spent the fifteen dollars she was going to use to buy the sloth on ammunition.

In the window she sees the reflection of her face. Then she sees his reflection in their apartment window, superimposed on the river-cranes. The cranes are sawing the sky, groaning forward and back. On the bed, he is thrashing back and forth, too.

I didn't mean to hurt you.

He is barely conscious, and gasping.

We're the same, she whispers.

Then she mopped up the blood, made him a torque bandage, took him to the hospital. Everywhere she looks in the ward malarial men lie like exhausted bread loaves. Whenever anyone is shot in the conflicts of the *garimpo*, the nearby gold mines, they are taken to the hospital in Belém.

'To your knowledge, has your husband ever had dengue, malaria, or HIV?' they say, when she fills out the forms. In

Portuguese, HIV sounds like *Ash ee va* – soft, almost
benevolent.

'We'd like to keep him overnight for observation and to run
blood tests,' the doctor tells her. 'It's just a grazing. He was
lucky. Or it was meant to be just that.'

When she told him the story about the robbers, the doctor
had shrugged.

'It happens a lot. And you live in a rich neighbourhood. You
should move downmarket. You can take him home in the
morning.'

The doctor looks at her, sudden and sharp. 'You're not
going to report this to the police, are you?'

'No.'

'Good.' He clips a piece of paper on to his board, turns
away from her. 'That would get you nowhere.'

She made sure he was asleep, then she walked out of the
hospital, caught a taxi and asked the driver to take her to the
ice cream parlour.

As I work my way through the riot-coloured ice creams –
Açai. Cajú. Cupuacú. Castanha – I run through the
possibilities of what I have begun to call My Future.

I will go and live with Lourdes and her brother. We will save
our money, the three of us, and I will take them to Miami.
There they will learn English, and instead of a prostitute
Lourdes will become a dark-skinned secretary in an
air-conditioned office.

I will leave this city. I will swim out to the one or two ships
that still make the journey up to Manaus and back again and
then are spat out of the mouth of the giant river, and go to
Port-of-Spain, to Monrovia, to Panama. There I will meet a
Belgian businessman in a bar and we will become lovers and
he will pay my passage home. Or I will go with him to
Antwerp and work there for the tourist board, guiding English
people around the city.

I will use all my savings to buy the sloth. I will return her to
the forest. I will journey for many days in small boats,

dependent upon the kindness of the people in the river settlements. They will understand what I am doing. They will help me. Even if by that point I smell of piss and green slime because the sloth will not let go, even at night, of my shoulders.

He had been out of the hospital for a week. The boy had just tripped into his trousers, closed the door. That night, like many nights before, she sat in the corner of the room, the one beside the tall faux-French window. She sat so that her hair was brushed lightly by the once-white gauzy curtains as they swung in the breeze. In front of her was the bed, which took up an obscenely large area of the room. Her legs – tanned, mosquito-bitten – were curled up underneath her, and she sank down as far as she could into the chair.

She loved to watch his face when he came close to orgasm. It twisted into an almost phantasmagoric mixture of pain and waiting. Waiting, waiting . . . and then relief. Like the slow opening of a flower, or the open mouths of bears, rabbits, small animals as they died, caught in the steel trap in the winter forests of her childhood.

She could do this, too. It wasn't just the boys she brought to him. They were made for each other. His penis was thin and long, delicate. She was small. They fit each other perfectly. Sweat even ran down their chests in synchronized rivulets.

In the morning she would change his wound. This would bind them more to each other. There was nothing about him that was foreign. Not his ruptured skin, the scar he would always carry. Every part of his anatomy seemed made to inhabit her body. And it had been even better between them, ever since he had told her she was not what he needed.

He watches her change the dressing on his wound, following the complex instructions from the doctor, which he could not understand because his Portuguese was bad. At these moments he looked at her face with an expression approaching benediction.

Later that night she lay beside him on the big bed, so hot she thought she might be breaking into a fever. She rolled over, away from him, careful not to touch his body. In the morning she got him a glass of water, took his gold-rimmed glasses delicately in her hands and cleaned them with her silk scarf. She replaced them gently on the bedside table.

Quietly, without looking him in the eye, she went around the room gathering her things. She stuffed them in her bag. The claustrophobia was getting worse with each second, but she tried not to appear rushed. He looked like a wounded animal, faultless and uncomprehending, lying tense and waiting for the moment to be over, the one when she would close the door behind her.

CREDIT BALANCE

0 = 00

EMBASSY OF KAZA
CONSULAR SEC
RECEIPT

Date: 29

Paid by

For A VISA

Signature

Nicholas Blincoe

My Kazakh Lover

X/O .NOT GOOD FOR PASSAGE FROM — CARRIER — FLIGHT — CLASS — DATE — TIME

Nicholas Blincoe is the author of four novels, including Manchester Slingback, winner of the CWA/Macallan Silver Dagger for Fiction. His latest novel, The Dope Priest, tells the story of a dope smuggler hiding out in Bethlehem and assuming the identity of a Catholic priest. Like all Rochdale-born men, Blincoe is deeply cosmopolitan.

The world is his cocktail lounge.

The telephone rang so weakly, it was almost begging to be ignored. I didn't know what to do. I could be losing face even noticing it. It rang again and I stood. On the third ring, I knew it was never going to rise above a pissy trilling so I picked up the receiver.

A woman's voice. She said, 'Please. Mr Edwards?'

'Yes. Speaking.'

'Please. I will be your translator. I am hired by Madam Iskakova.'

I said, 'OK then. Down to business at last.'

When I touched down at Almaty airport yesterday, Shirin Iskakova had been waiting for me. I pushed through the crowds of taxi touts with their tarnished gold teeth, burnished with nicotine, and saw her there. A small round woman, she looked like Buddha in drag except that she wore her coat gangster-style, draped across her shoulders. In the context, her young driver seemed more like a bodyguard: a genuine gangster's bodyguard, because she gave the impression that he was only there for decoration – if she really needed him, she would never have become a don in the first place.

She didn't seem surprised to see me, although I soon realized that she hadn't got the message about my boss and the mild heart attack that was keeping him close to bedridden. She just nodded at me, eyes narrowed, the exact same way she would nod as she flicked through the rows of coats at our Walthamstow showroom, blandly and buddhically inscrutable as she examined the men's winter range. Over the past three years, she had bought enough coats to make this return visit necessary. Jez sent his apologies, a brief run-through of his medical condition and the news that a young, capable man, Mr Edwards – me –

would travel to Kazakhstan in his place. He dictated the
message over the phone, I e-mailed it to Shirin Iskakova. If
Jez had been able to send the message himself, it would
have been in Russian. His version of Word allowed him to
convert the keyboard to Cyrillic script. I didn't have that
option, but then I didn't have any Russian either, as Shirin
Iskakova found out at the airport. She didn't seem impressed
by my unilingual status. That's when I first began to feel I was
losing face.

Iskakova only said, 'Mr Jeremy. No?'

I shook my head: no.

We drove the fifteen minutes to Almaty in silence. I rested
my head on the window and watched the night dilute to a
thin autumn mist. It wasn't much of a dawn but I didn't care.
My body clock knew it was really only midnight. I was
suffering, and Iskakova's driver wasn't helping me
acclimatize. He drove with a careless speed, flicking his long
fringe out of his eyes as he raced corners and dropping to a
baby crawl whenever he had to bump across the inlaid steel
tramlines in the road. Iskakova remained impassive, up front,
staring ahead with the same bland face. She wasn't even
wearing a seat-belt.

It was Jez's idea to rent an apartment rather than stay in a
hotel. His reasoning: only the international hotels would be
comfortable and they would cost international prices. Shirin
Iskakova arranged everything; the apartment would cost
twenty-five dollars a night. More than a month's wages for
the average city worker, but for that price we got a central
apartment, one bedroom, kitchen–dining room, with a
large-sized refrigerator and a living room with a Japanese TV,
parquet floor throughout. Iskakova's driver carried my bag up
the crumbling concrete steps to the fourth floor of what could
have been a council block and opened the apartment doors,
inner and outer, both with good locks. He then dropped the
keys into my hand and took a pace back, leaving Shirin
Iskakova to follow me through, room by room.

After the stairwell, the apartment was a surprise. It was

clean, and though it was old-fashioned, only the bathroom
was archaic. Iskakova muttered a few words over every
room, then muttered a final thing at the doorway before
shrugging and leaving. I hung a few shirts on hangers before I
began experimenting with the telephone. After five minutes, I
assumed it didn't work. Three hours later, Shirin Iskakova's
translator explained that most telephones were adapted to
make only citywide calls, which were free of charge.

'I need to make an international call. I have to call my boss,
Mr Jeremy.'

I heard muttering. Then the translator came back on line. 'I
understand. But now, Madam Iskakova says it is four a.m.
London time. So she will send a car for you and we will have
lunch and meet members of the business community. Then
you will make your telephone calls on an international
telephone.'

It was October 31st, Hallowe'en. The weak dawn didn't even
hint at what a beautiful autumn day this Hallowe'en was
going to be. The air was crisp, and the city was so heavily
tree-lined, the streets were carpeted with leaves. But it was
the mountains surrounding Almaty that really stole the show:
thrown against the blue sky, capped with snow and trimmed
with forests, modelling the whole colour chart of red through
orange. We ate lunch outside, in a wooden gazebo behind a
roadside restaurant half-way up a mountain. The restaurant
served shashlik, barbecued on broad skewers. Everyone ate
with enthusiasm – me, Shirin Iskakova, another woman the
translator introduced as Zhumagul, and the translator herself,
who was called Olga. Olga was Russian, or her grandparents
were. She was a pale nineteen, she studied English and
Tourism at Almaty University. Both Shirin Iskakova and
Zhumagul were oriental, although in different ways. Iskakova
had a broad but small nose and her black hair was cut so
that it feathered around her very round face. Zhumagul had a
bigger nose, bigger lips, in all, a much bigger head. Her hair
was naturally brown streaked with non-natural highlights. I

was finding out for myself what Jez had told me before I left London, that Kazakhstan is a radically mixed nation, everyone looks different to everyone else. The things they have in common: they take a long time to get down to business, they like to begin by building personal relationships. He then warned me to do my very best to pay my way. No one from Kazakhstan ever likes to see anyone else pick up a bill. I thought I would establish a natural order this first lunch-time and asked Olga to request the bill as soon as our plates were cleared. Olga explained that it had already been paid.

I smiled around the table. 'Please thank Madam Iskakova on my behalf.'

A moment later, Olga said, 'Madam Iskakova asks that you call her Shirin.'

Lunch was followed by a tour of a department store, a Soviet-era block-wide building now divided into separate boutiques. Zhumagul's shop stocked only Italian clothes, which wasn't a surprise. It wasn't easy getting a competitive edge against Milan, but I shared some of Jez's confidence in our new menswear range. It was growing dark now, about five o'clock Kazakhstan time, and I still hadn't managed to speak to Jez, but I was no longer worried. With Olga translating I didn't feel as needy and inadequate. And anyway, until I saw one of Shirin's own shops I had nothing to report back. I was still concentrating on the business of building relations. Jez's advice again: no one from Kazakhstan would ever try to rip me off. He told me they always deal fairly and honestly, and they do that by making sure there is a basic level of trust before negotiations begin. Then the negotiations themselves, they could be hard, actually, bloody hard, but there was nothing underhand.

So we celebrated Hallowe'en – a smaller party than I expected after the rounds of introductions throughout the afternoon. It was just Olga, myself and Shirin. Our coats were taken in the foyer, and we walked downstairs to be greeted by a hollow pumpkin head, sat on a barrel. The restaurant was new, done out in an Alpine style, blond wood

everywhere, Grolsch and Bitburger at the bar, but a menu
that was firmly Kazakh. I began with lagman, a noodle and
meat soup, followed by manty, beetroot salad with large
oriental dumplings. Olga had the same, except that her main
course was roast pike. She shared a bottle of Pinot Noir with
me. Shirin had red caviar followed by cured horsemeat. To
drink, she had camel milk. For afters, she proposed having
me.

'How's that?'

Now Olga was blushing, 'Madam Iskakova wishes you to
know that she finds you attractive.'

'Oh? Yeah?'

'And she would like you to spend the night with her.'
Olga's face was flushed through. I don't know how she
managed to keep her voice so steady.

'That is . . . It is . . . Tell her she is very kind' – I was
stammering like a comedy vicar – 'but please excuse me, I
need to go to the bathroom.'

I stood at the basin, throwing handfuls of cold water into
my face, staring at myself in the mirror, dripping away. I didn't
know what Shirin saw in me. I knew I was terrified of her. I
didn't want to be alone with her. Forget about intimacy.

I was thinking of ways to reassert an equilibrium. I hung
about the archway that led to the dining area, trying to catch
my waiter's eye without being seen by Shirin. I thought that if
I could pay the bill now, I would have gained a measure of
control. As the waiter came sailing by, I took his arm and
hissed, 'Cheque? Bill?'

He shook his head. I tried to remember the Russian word
but couldn't. So I mimed writing, making a note on my palm
with an invisible biro.

The waiter nodded back towards the dining room. I peered
around the arch and saw Shirin stack a wad of notes on a
silver plate. The bill had been settled.

We left Olga at the restaurant. Shirin Iskakova and I made the
short taxi ride to her apartment alone, together. She lived on

the eighth floor of a tower block, not far from my own apartment. The block seemed as ordinary as any other, except that the cars outside were Mercedes, Toyotas and Range Rovers, and the foyer was guarded by armed men. There was nothing unusual about the lift itself, a rattling box made of dent-easy tin. At the eighth floor, we stepped out into a landing with yellowy walls and a plastic-tiled floor. The landing would have held four apartments, but only one of the door frames still held an actual door. The other three were walled up. I found out why when Shirin showed me around her apartment. It covered the whole of the floor, wrapped around the lift and stair shaft like a doughnut wrapped around its hole.

The largest room was the dining room, big enough for the fourteen-seater table that made it seem like an executive boardroom. Shirin interrupted the tour of the apartment for a moment, asking me: 'Vodka? Cognac?'

The drinks cabinet was built into the wall, mounted beneath a glowing fish tank. I looked at the bottles and chose cognac. Although Shirin was a Muslim, she decided to join me. She took a vodka, which she sipped as she led me through to the last room. Her bedroom.

She pressed herself against me, wrapping her arms around my body and clasping them at the small of my neck. I bent low, making up the ten-inch height difference between us. My thin, dry English lips met her damp and squashy lips. Her face was squashy, too. The sharp bones of my face sank into her soft chipmunk cheeks. There was no clash of pointy noses. Then she unclenched me and pushed me towards the bed.

She wore a short cream camisole under her trouser suit. Her small breasts pouted beneath it, looking in opposite directions. Her belly wasn't so large, but it began just beneath her breasts and ended just below the elastic of her French knickers without pausing for a waistline. Her legs were sturdy but, I noticed, slightly bandy. She waddled the two paces to the bed where I sat wearing nothing but a slight

chest rash and a pair of underpants. I didn't see any reason
to remove the underpants; she would find out how limp I
was, soon enough.

She put her hands on my shoulders and pushed me down.
As I went back, I hunched up the bed so my feet were clear
of the floor. I lay there, draped like a noodle strand,
wondering exactly how delectable I could look. Shirin had her
knees either side of my body. She crawled up me. I didn't
know what she intended, whether she would pause when our
groins met or whether she would continue until we were
face-to-face. I closed my eyes and counted. When I opened
them again, I found myself looking up like one of those
frightened witnesses in a science-fiction film, watching
Shirin's body pass above me like a flying saucer crossing the
island of Manhattan.

I thought, 'Oh.' Maybe I even said it, but my mouth was
soon smothered in the silky nap of her French knickers. She
pressed forward, making herself comfortable before she
released me slightly and slipped a finger under the crotch of
her panties. As she pulled the material back, she gave me
time for one breath before she pushed herself on to my
unilingual tongue.

I woke up alone. After taking a shower, I heard a noise
coming from the kitchen and was surprised to find Olga. She
was cooking scrambled egg and diced sausage. It was all for
me, but as she served she refused to catch my eye and
spoke in staccato sentences of tics and dots. Madam
Iskakova was at a meeting . . . Madam Iskakova hoped to
meet me for lunch . . . Perhaps I would like to visit the
mountains again . . . Or the Gallery of Modern Art . . . Or the
National Park of Fairground Amusements.

Over the next three days, Shirin's driver took me to all
those places. In between tourist trips I made brief visits to
three of Shirin's shops and looked at the well-stocked rails of
men's Italian winter coats in dismay. I was still having trouble
reaching Jez, handicapped because I didn't want to phone

between eight in the evening and eleven in the morning, London time, assuming that his condition required plenty of rest. But with the six-hour time difference between London and Almaty and the scarcity of international telephones, I never felt I was in the right place at the right time to put in the call. Maybe I was making more of the problem than I needed to. I kept telling myself if I could get together with Shirin again, I could persuade her to make a large order. My fervour would carry us through from the act of love to the closing of the deal. I had fervour coming out of my ears.

Shirin Iskakova was a real lover. I'd spent passive chunks of my life thinking about sex: how much I wanted it and whether there was any way to get more of it. Rarely thinking about the thing itself, never as something with its own energy, its own grace and beauty. The way Shirin made love, I could kick myself for all those times I made ungainly English love, self-consciously spidering my elbows and knees around the bed. But I didn't want to beat myself up. I was a bigger character now, I had glimpsed the intensity of physical love. And I began to prickle with ideas, all the ways I could give and share pleasure. If I got a fucking chance.

The closest I got to Shirin was on the second day, when she organized a banquet in my honour. With Olga stuttering through the translations, Shirin told me she had invited many other businesswomen, all perhaps of use to me and to Mr Jeremy. I thanked her, directly, holding her eyes as I said the words. 'Thank you for everything.'

I sat through the first three courses, laying down my knife and fork every few minutes for the different toasts. I had to prod Olga to translate the speeches. Some of the speeches raised tears from the other guests, some got big laughs. But Olga translated them all into adolescent attitude.

'She asks we drink to England.'

'We drink now to friends, also to loyalty in general.'

'He drinks to Kazakhstan women, who are interesting.'

The men at the table, the husbands of these prominent businesswomen, were civil servants, even a minister and a

chief of police. But they earned state wages. It was the
women who made the money that paid for the cars, the
mobile phones, the new suits and the improved dentistry.

I took my chance when the plates were being cleared
before the main course. I stood, made my way to the
bathroom but leapt sideways to the kitchen. Shirin and her
maid were arranging a dish that looked like lasagne pasta
and boiled meat. I moved around Shirin, to the blind side of
the maid, and put my palm against the small of her back.

Shirin turned around sharply and fixed me with a look. Her
eyes carried the universal signal: No means No. I pulled back
my hand as fast as if it had been scalded. Locked in the
toilet, I stared in the mirror until my colour normalized and my
eyes stopped stinging.

Back in the room, the boiled-meat dish was almost served.
Only one plate remained and Shirin was serving that herself: it
sat in front of a baggily fat man in his sixties. He nodded
when his plate was full and then Shirin lifted her glass.

Olga translated, 'She drinks to her husband, who is good
and wise.'

I looked at Olga. Her lips straightened into a mean smile as
she said, 'Shirin says her husband is strong.'

I looked back up the table. The old man might well have
been strong, but we were talking about past days.

Olga said, 'He has given her five beautiful children.'

I turned back to Olga, who hissed a final few words: facts
this time, not a part of her translation. 'He lives on the floor
below with the two children who are not yet at University.'

I couldn't get any more information. I didn't want to
question Olga too closely, even the next day when she and
the driver took me for lunch and another trip to the bowling
hall. I just didn't want to give the girl any more reason to sulk.
I don't know why she was so offended by Shirin. Perhaps she
wasn't. Perhaps it was just her nature because she acted as
sourly towards the driver as she did towards me. She sat out
during the bowling, sucking primly at the straw that pierced
her bucket of Coca-Cola. I played three rounds with the

driver without asking a single question, saving her the trouble
of actually doing any work.

When my wrist was too swollen to continue playing, I
turned to Olga and said, 'OK.'

As I was washing my hands, Shirin's driver paid for the
bowling game. I felt mildly guilty, more annoyed. I knew I was
getting slack about paying my way. Most of the time, I just left
it, sometimes even forgetting to thank whoever had paid.
Now, I frowned at the driver and gave him a curt 'thank you'.
It was Shirin's money, she was paying to keep me distantly
amused.

The car pulled up by a row of three shops at Gogol and
Communist. About the only money I had spent since arriving
in Almaty was the twelve tenge a guy in a street kiosk had
charged me for a map of the city grid. The map was
hand-drawn and photocopied, but I could make out the
handwriting well enough to know that Communist Street was
no longer called Communist Street. It was just that everyone
still used the old name. I heard it often enough; even I had
managed to catch it and memorize it. Gogol and Communist
was about as central an address as any in the city. The
shops proved it. The first shop was a *parfumerie*, advertising
Chanel, YSL, Dior. The second shop was a Boss franchise.
The third shop was empty. I followed the driver into the third
shop. Shirin was there ahead of me.

I almost wanted to chase her around the shop, see if I
could corral her in one of the changing rooms. But the shop
was so new, the cubicles still had no curtains. Any passer-by
could see us from the street. As for the driver and Olga, they
could see us wherever they looked. There were enough
mirrors to frame us, reflect us, distort my fumblings.

Instead, I offered Shirin credit. This was a large and empty
store; it needed stocking – and not with anything
Italian-made. Olga translated my offer: we could give her fifty
thousand dollars credit, she could fill this place and pay us,
say, three months down the line.

Shirin listened and sent her reply back around the circuit. It was an interesting offer, she would happily take ten thousand dollars credit.

I couldn't help myself. I burst out, saying: 'No. She's never spent as little as ten thousand dollars on any trip to Walthamstow. And there she pays cash. Why would I come all the way to Almaty to offer credit?' Then I stopped, feeling the pulse at the back of my neck, the artery wide open and slamming the blood to my head. I didn't want to show my nerves. If I didn't keep calm, it might be all over.

Shirin's answer, via Olga: 'She sympathizes. She had hoped you would find other customers among her friends in business. But these are not good times. It is unfortunate.'

'Tell her I can't give her just ten thousand dollars credit.'

Olga said, 'Madam Iskakova says that she wishes to help. But she has room in her boutiques for only overcoats to the value of ten thousand dollars.'

'That's nothing.'

'She has no more room. It will be a tight squeeze.'

I held open my arms, 'This shop is enormous.'

Olga didn't wait for anything to translate. 'This is not Madam Iskakova's boutique. It is the boutique of Nursultan.'

I stared at her. It just wasn't clicking through my head fast enough, there was too much blood up there.

Shirin was speaking. Olga translated, 'If you agree, Madam Iskakova will take ten thousand dollars credit and Nursultan will take forty thousand dollars.'

I turned and looked at Shirin, and then at the driver. He was Nursultan, I had heard his name often but had never used it myself. And I realized now that he wasn't a driver. He was the man who had entertained me for three days, taking me on the rides at the state fair, paying for my bowling games, feeding me up to three times a day. Even buying the vodkas and beers I drank in grumpy silence every night before I staggered up the four floors to my lonely bed.

'Tell Mr Nursultan that his shop is very beautiful,' I said. I paused; Olga paused, too. She knew I had not finished yet. 'And tell him we would be happy to offer him terms.'

Olga was still silent, looking at me expectantly . . .

I turned to my left, pinching the bridge of my nose. The whole of my headache seemed to have gathered in that one spot. Bent slightly, I was staring into a mirror. The mirror bounced back the reflection of Shirin, her hand holding Nursultan's buttocks in a soft caress.

'Forty thousand dollars credit,' I said. 'Satisfied.'

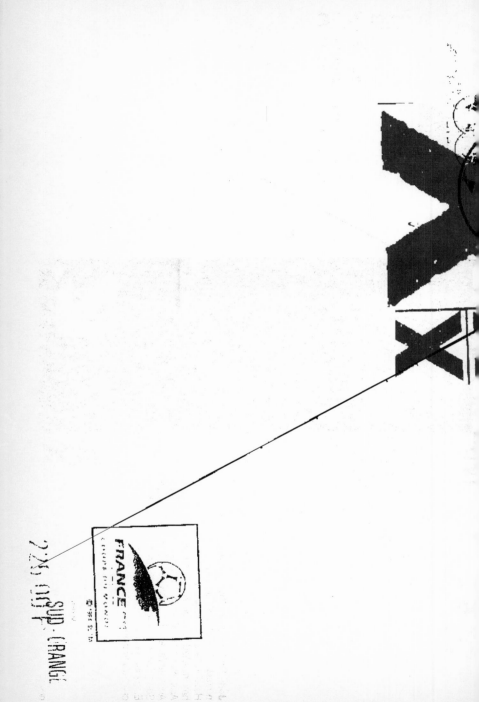

FRANCE 98
LA COUPE DU MONDE

SUD - ORANGE

225.000 F

ANGLETERRE / TUNISIE

John King
The Beasts of Marseille

John King is the author of three novels, The Football Factory, Headhunters and England Away. He has travelled extensively in Europe, Asia, North and Central America and Australasia, and has crossed the former Soviet Union on the Trans-Siberian Express. He lives in London and is currently working on a fourth

novel.

Robert Bradley sipped his cocktail and stared through the polished window of the hotel's Executive Bar. He was enjoying his time in Marseille, the fine cuisine and sophisticated locals adding to the pleasure of his assignment covering the England football team's stay in the city. Anything he wanted was available on expenses. Anything at all. He had six tickets in his room for tomorrow's game and was meeting his contacts beforehand in one of Marseille's most exclusive restaurants. Rob adjusted his legs, but kept his gaze focused on the English Hooligan sprawled across the pavement outside, a group of Arab youths kicking the unconscious man about the head and body. Rob rolled the tequila-mix around his mouth and savoured the texture. He tried not to leer, but it slipped out, the pressure in his groin growing with each blow to the English Hooligan's body. The lout had cropped hair and was wearing a cheap pair of shorts, with what seemed to be a Union Jack motif. Rob was filled with disgust at the sight of what he considered a racist symbol. He thought he spied a tattoo, a shield and trident, but wasn't sure. The man was quite obviously a fascist, a violent imperialist thug preying on defenceless minorities. As a respected journalist on a publication which termed itself 'left-of-centre', Rob never considered walking outside to try and help the man, who was now being slowly targeted. He felt his scrotum tighten as one of the Arabs jumped on the man's left knee, trying to smash the joint, another strolling forward with a thick length of wood which he bounced off the Hooligan's head, the loud crack reaching Rob's ears. A flush of excitement raced down the journalist's spine. He noticed a small pool of blood forming and, captivated, watched it trickle across the street, musing on life, death and the liberating literature of William S. Burroughs. His penis was ready to burst out of his flies as the beating continued, waves of political righteousness surging through his nervous system, energizing his very being, the thought of the English Hooligan receiving his just desserts at the hands of an oppressed ethnic group filling him with the sort of intense arousal he had only ever experienced in what his publication described as 'radical sado-masochism'. Rob Bradley hated these oiks. He hated their crass lager culture and lack of respect for educated liberals such as himself, detested the thumping music and cheap high-street fashion, the vulgar language and illegal chemicals, the promiscuity and willingness to travel on the cheap. Not that he would term it this way. He wanted to see the common folk do well, of course he did, preferring the easy option of attributing right-wing politics to them to explain his prejudice to the obvious explanation that he was one more stuck-up snob. The sexual excitement was incredible, and Rob was struggling to control himself, silently cursing as he blew his beans into the crotch of a hundred-pound pair of silk boxer shorts. He prayed that he hadn't stained the label, deeply regretting this familiar lack of control. He wished his arousal had lasted a little longer, that he could have maximized the pleasure and timed his ejaculation to coincide with a final neck-breaking stomp. Rob consoled himself with the fact that the gendarmes were still nowhere to be seen. The beating continued, and he wondered if the man would die, or perhaps spend the rest of his life confined to a wheelchair, dismissing the English Hooligan from his mind as the reality of his own situation struck home. He had more important matters to consider than mere life and death, faced as he was with the tricky business of negotiating the hotel foyer without his little accident being detected. Luckily the drinks were billed to his account, and he didn't have to pass reception to reach the lift. His penis was still stiff, but his testicles were expanding, the prick of barbed wire beginning to sting. Rob loved consensual pain, but his erection withered as he spied a gang of English Football Hooligans, the very mindless element he so despised. Rob hated violence and felt the sickness rise in his throat as the scum moved forward, jumping to his feet and hurrying off to his room.

Gary came around the corner and spotted Phil on the floor, surrounded by a French mob which was kicking the shit out of the bloke. He turned and called to the rest of the boys, and twenty England piled in. Gary was first on the scene, his fist connecting with a shaved head, the French turning from Phil's battered body and fronting up the English. A greasy slag with a lump of wood stepped forward and was taken out by Jesus, a long-haired Villa boy, the man hitting the deck and given no time to recover, kicked about the head and body. For thirty seconds it was toe-to-toe fighting before the French turned and legged it in the opposite direction. Gary and Tony tried to pull Phil to his feet, but he was in a bad way, his body heavy and legs limp. There was a police van approaching, so Mills and Jesus came over, and the four of them carried Phil past the posh hotels and restaurants lining the boulevard, ducking down the first alley-way they saw. The sound of clucking lingered in their ears as respectable onlookers shook their heads in disgust, Tony pointing out that these were the sort of decent citizens who were quite happy to vote for Le Pen and deny French collaboration with the Nazis, but found themselves outraged by crude Anglo-Saxon swear-words and a healthy love of lager. The England boys were soon lost in the side-streets, a maze of older stone corridors with none of the pretence of the street they'd left behind. Once they were confident they weren't being tracked by the French old bill, they settled Phil on a doorstep. There was blood all over his shirt, but he was moving a bit, starting to come round.

Jason Rodgers stepped back into a doorway as the English Yobs disappeared and a police van skidded to a halt. Gendarmes jumped out of the back, and Jason's skin tingled

as he noted the authoritative squelch of polished leather on
concrete. The police closed the area and began approaching
bystanders for information, the expensive boutiques and
bistros spewing out a small wave of well-heeled folk who
hadn't actually witnessed the incident but were nevertheless
sickened by the behaviour of the English. Jason smiled and
tucked his camera in its case. He had a roll of film showing
the English Yobs engaged in hand-to-hand combat on
foreign streets, strutting around like they owned the place, on
the rampage without an officer class to point out officially
sanctioned targets. There was no method or organization to
the madness. The Yobs were an undisciplined rabble heaping
shame on a proud military tradition which had been hard-won
by the front-line bravery and selflessness of the aristocracy. It
was quite outrageous, but Jason couldn't stand around
bemoaning the uncivilized behaviour of the proles. There was
money to be made and a career to enhance. He had to get
the pictures back to London pronto. He strode across the
road and entered the hotel opposite, marched to reception
and asked if they had the technology to wire his images to
London. Jason was led to the lift and up to an office where
he was able to view the operation. His editor would be
ecstatic and Jason knew he was on to a winner. The right-
wing publication which paid his expenses and a very healthy
retainer would gobble up the pictures. He knew the key
phrases that would be applied off by heart – 'mindless thugs',
'hooligan shame', 'a disgrace to the nation', and his own
favourite, which echoed the wisdom of Wellington, 'scum of
the earth'. Jason rubbed his crotch and admired the arse of
the young French assistant. Although a one-hundred-per-
cent heterosexual, with a wife and two children, Jason was
nevertheless willing to bugger any of his social inferiors who
showed willing. He licked his lips, but quickly dismissed the
notion. There was plenty of time for that later. He was a
professional and had to see the job through. He had certainly
braved the odds, watching the initial beating of the lone
Englishman impassively as he searched for a suitable

restaurant in which to eat, but had been alert enough to begin snapping once the English Yobs arrived on the scene, petrified in case these violent thugs took exception to having their photographs taken. These idiots had little understanding of the importance of a free press in a democratic society, the valuable role the media played in controlling abuses of power and reporting matters essential to the well-being of the nation, the need for truth and justice that overruled all personal and financial considerations. Jason ran his tongue over dry lips. Once back in London, the photos would be skilfully cropped and distorted by the art department, a clever sub-editor would add a snappy caption, and one of the paper's numerous on-the-scene reporters would construct an outraged story which incorporated all those clichés the publisher loved. His photos would set off the usual chain reaction, as columnists short of ideas spotted an easy target for their vitriol and a welcome source of wordage. The story would run for days, spreading across television screens and into the House of Commons. Politicians would jump on the bandwagon, irrespective of party loyalties and, who knows, a senior government figure might even pop over to France for a spot of arse-licking.

Phil was in a bad way, his head lolling and eyes rolling. Gary wondered if his neck was broken, but reasoned that if it was, then they'd know by now. Two old women came out of a door opposite, their faces creased and weathered, specks of grey in jet-black hair. They brought a bowl of water and a towel, sat next to Phil and dabbed at his face, cleaning the blood away and patting his bruises. Several old men followed. Gary looked up at the parched stone, the open windows and cool shadow, long shafts of light playing across the walls. He could hear music, and then a fuzzy voice. These people were from a North African background, same as the mob who'd attacked Phil, but they had a different approach to visitors. They were older, and curious rather than angry. Jesus was leaning against a wall with Tony and Mills, all three

catching their breath after the punch-up. Jesus began talking
with one of the men, who said his name was Mohammed.
Gary had to smile. Jesus and Mohammed having a chat
down a Marseille back-alley. Next thing Joan of Arc would
come wandering along in her body armour. Mohammed
asked Jesus what had happened, and the Holte End greaser
explained about Phil and the mob who'd attacked him for no
good reason. Mohammed explained that Marseille was a
rough town, that the locals had been told the English were on
their way, and that the image of the travelling English football
fan was of a drunk skinhead who hated anyone who wasn't
white. Gary reasoned that it wasn't much of a surprise the
locals were game for a row. It was mental really, because the
way he saw it, it was the Vichy French who'd helped out the
Nazis during the war, Germany and Italy who had the strong
right-wing parties today, along with France. It was predictable
enough. The cunts in the media back home promoted the
same stereotype, so you couldn't really expect their French
equivalent to have enough imagination to scout out the truth.
He could understand a mob-on-mob confrontation, but had
no time for wankers battering the fuck out of someone on
their own, especially the likes of Phil, a peaceful bloke who
loved bumming around Europe and experiencing different
cultures. Some of the others had walked down the road to
have a look and were waiting on the corner, while Phil seemed
to be perking up. His face was a mess, and in an ideal world
he'd probably have gone along to the local hospital for a
once-over, but it was risky. It seemed like the whole of
Marseille was on the war-path, and they didn't want to end
up getting deported for defending themselves. Gary noticed
other faces appearing from windows as word spread, started
to get a bit nervous. All they needed was a younger, larey
element to come along and they'd be in the shit, closed in by
the buildings. Right on cue, a group of youths appeared.
They approached Mohammed, who spoke in Arabic. They
nodded and looked interested, but kept their distance.

*

It was pure chance that Rob Bradley and Jason Rodgers bumped into each other. Jason had wired his pictures back to London, while Rob had showered and changed his soiled boxer shorts, before calling his office and relating an eyewitness account of the barbaric behaviour of the English Hooligans in welcoming, genteel Marseille. There was a small nick from the barbed wire, but nothing Rob couldn't handle. The two men had met in the lift and retired to the Executive Bar for a refreshing drink, their day's work done. Although they served publications purporting to represent vastly opposing political views, both Rob and Jason were adult enough not to let their beliefs seep into real life. They squabbled over whose publication should buy the drinks and were soon settled into two comfortable leather armchairs next to the window. They discussed the English Hooligans and English Yobs rampaging through the streets of Marseille, shaking their heads in sadness, two respectable and honest men digging deep to find the truth, their front-row seats providing the perfect position from which to pass judgement.

The England boys split up, with Gary, Phil, Jesus and Tony going back to the hostel for a wash-up and some food before a night on the piss. Phil needed to lie down, sleep off the shock and let his battered body recover. It was no fun having a mob kicking you to pieces. He was shaking, and his vision was blurred. They were staying in a cheap four-bed room, two bunks and a window overlooking a mangy street corner stacked with rubbish. Phil lay down on his bunk and in seconds was asleep. Gary went down the hall and stood under the shower. At first the water was warm, the tank heated by the sun, but it soon turned cold. He washed the dust away, humming the tune from *The Great Escape*, before moving into *The Dam Busters*. Revitalized, he dried off and dressed, ready for a feed and a decent drink. They left Phil and went three doors down to a couscous cafe, each filling up on food that reminded them of the curries back home. If curry was England's national dish, then couscous had to represent the best of French cuisine. It was better than all that other muck, the dead horses and snails. Fucking horrible. Mind you, the bread was good. Same with the cheese. But the boys were used to something with a bit of spice, and the owner of the cafe, who introduced himself as Mohammed, was impressed by the amount of chilli they were sliding down. At first he was cautious, but more friendly once he realized they weren't going to wreck the gaff. It was a pity, but showed the power of the media to distort and fuck things up. It didn't matter where you were, whether it was England, France or whatever, there was always a media class creating tension, same as there was a political class. Bollocks to all that; what upset the boys most was the way the French had made it so hard to get tickets, the touts taking the piss. None of them had tickets, and they were getting worried. Usually it was easy, but here they were, the day before the England game, and they hadn't had a sniff yet. Word had gone round that the hotels, trains and bars had jacked their prices up. They were being ripped off, and it left a bad taste. The hostel was cheap and cheerful and lacked the snobbishness they'd found elsewhere. But bollocks to all that as well; with the couscous and bread filling their guts, they didn't give a toss about fine points, were looking forward to a drink and a sing-song. Jesus paid Mohammed and they went back to the hostel for Phil. He was still asleep and shaking, running through a nightmare replay. They left him and headed for the bar where they'd arranged to meet the others.

Jason and Rob examined the wine list, and Rob ordered in perfect French. Once the fifty-pound bottle of fizz had arrived and been sampled, they consulted the menu. For starters they ordered *pâté de foie gras*, followed by blood-red steaks. The two respected journalists clinked their glasses and toasted their essential roles in the world. Their chests puffed out as they revelled in a heart-warming sense of their own importance.

*

After two days drinking hypermarket miniatures in Calais,
Gary and the boys were glad to get some tap lager down
their throats. The measures could've been a bit more
generous, but you had to adapt when you were overseas,
respect the local culture. The lager wasn't cheap, but it was
stronger than at home, and after a couple had taken effect
they forgot about the price. They were on tour and weren't
going to stand about moaning all night. That was for the
wannabe hippies who spent two hours bartering with
dirt-poor Asian peasants over five pence. Gary hated wealthy
travellers pretending they were poor. There were a few of
them back in the hostel, sitting in the foyer comparing
passport stamps and swapping diarrhoea stories. Still, that
was their problem; Gary and the boys were more interested
in the night ahead. The bar was packed with a good two
hundred England, another couple of hundred spilling along
the street outside. There was a familiar feeling in the air, and it
was obvious there was going to be trouble later on. The
nearby bars were stacked, a line of riot police watching from
across the street. Jesus was getting some friendly stick off a
couple of Sunderland skins, who said it was odd meeting a
long-haired Villa fan. Jesus was a friendly enough bloke and
smiled as he poured more lager down his throat. A couple of
Cross of St Georges had been draped over a wall, and the
owner and bar staff looked nervous but were going along
with things, seeing as how they were coining it. They were
more used to serving yachting types who made a glass of
wine last two hours. The bar was soon singing IF IT
WASN'T FOR THE ENGLISH YOU'D BE KRAUTS
again and again, broken up with the classics RULE
BRITANNIA and THERE'LL ALWAYS BE AN
ENGLAND. For the first time since he'd left Dover, Gary was
seriously glad to be in France. That's what it was like. You
went through all the months of saving up, the grief of
Customs and working out the Paris Métro, the boring journey
south sitting up all night with a stiff neck and itchy socks, the
long wander trying to find a place to sleep when nobody

wanted to help you out, all the hassle along the way, and you
started wondering what the fucking point was, and then,
bang, there you were in the middle of another England away.
It was suddenly all worth while, and everyone was in the
same boat. Making the francs stretch, knowing the English
were hated wherever they went, but fuck all these cunts
anyway, IF IT WASN'T FOR THE ENGLISH YOU'D BE
KRAUTS. Gary felt the anger rise up. This was a country the
English had bailed out in the war, two world wars, and what
did they do? Wouldn't even sell you a ticket for a fucking
football match. They were branded as hooligans before
they'd even left home. What was the point of that? He
thought of the aggro in Gare du Sud with that Paris-St
Germaine mob. The look of the passengers on the train to
Marseille when they'd gone into first class by mistake. The
young ones had been all right, and the families sitting up all
night, travelling cheap – they were sweet as well, wanted a
laugh like anyone else – and the sexy French accents of the
girls got everyone going, but those snobs who hated the
drinking and singing and laughter did his head in. Fuck it, he
didn't want to get into all that, didn't want to get wound up,
but he was worried about not getting into the game. He saw
Jesus lean over the bar when the bartenders were down the
other end and fill five glasses, hand them out, redistributing
wealth and questioning the established order. This cheered
Gary up. The strange thing was, he genuinely liked France.
He'd been to Paris on a weekender, and he'd had a blinding
time. That bird he'd pulled. Fucking beautiful. You didn't get
that back in Tooting. The voice was what did it for Gary. The
French accent. He was going to look her up on the way
home, but couldn't think of that right now. He was in
Marseille for the football and, truth be told, no woman in her
right mind was going to walk into this bar packed with
hundreds of England boys out on the piss.

Rob and Jason polished off the champagne and got to work.
The boy on the bed had reduced his price after twenty

minutes of hard bartering by the journos, and the two men were raring to go. The kid was probably under-age, but they hadn't asked so couldn't be held responsible for any mistakes. He was of North African extraction, Rob seeing the youth as a brave libertine from an ancient desert society which rejected the conservative restraints of his own repressive culture. He thought of the Beats, imagined the poverty of Tangier. Rob felt as if he were part of an artistic élite, a free-thinker sent to help the poor with generous hand-outs, a kindred spirit who understood the ways of the world, an international traveller, an adventurer. Jason, meanwhile, saw the boy as a dirty faggot who deserved everything he was about to get. These people would do anything for money. Jason hated homosexuals and considered his role in the coming affair as nothing more than a display of power, his chance to abuse the non-white hordes who threatened to swarm all over Europe and bring Christendom to its knees. With a second bottle of champagne chilling in the ice bucket, the two hacks were soon in action, Rob at one end, Jason the other, the two journalists instantly moving to a common rhythm, their much promoted differences forgotten. It didn't take long before a roar of mutual satisfaction filled the air-conditioned room, the two media-whores achieving simultaneous orgasm at the expense of the cringing rent boy.

The second canister blew a hole in the window, but by now most of the English were out in the street, taunting the old bill. Gary and the boys hung about till a stand-off developed, the riot police popping off tear gas and the English lobbing bottles. Jesus took command of Gary and the others, and they drifted away from the glare of publicity, back through the alley-ways till they found a quiet bar, leaving the glass-throwers and window-smashers to put on a show. Cameras were busy recording the drama from behind police lines, the wires buzzing as the international media started on a feeding frenzy, the mob who'd come along and kicked things off by taunting the English long gone. Gary and the boys settled down for a drink, and inside half an hour the bar had filled up with like-minded English, the more sussed element who understood that the real action would come later on, away from the riot police and media lens. There were a few scores needed settling.

Ali smiled but felt sick inside. His customers were sitting in chairs, their bodies covered in slime, revelling in their nakedness. They reminded him of the beasts in the butcher's window, except these two had escaped the slaughterer's knife. One of the men opened another bottle of champagne but didn't bother offering Ali a glass. He looked at the two men with disgust, dressed and waited for his money. They were playing games with him. One was contemptuous, while the other seemed hurt, as though the question of payment somehow ruined the experience. The boy was familiar with these types and had little patience. He had been driven to prostitution by poverty, in desperation, and hated the acts he was forced to endure. The man with the look of disgust on his face was typical of his wealthy right-wing clients, while the one with the hurt expression was a liberal fool who believed Ali's work was somehow connected with personal choice. His self-control soon deserted him. They were the lowest form of life. He pretended he was going to the bathroom, then turned and buried his knife in the heart of the man with the sneer. The bloated body crashed to the floor, and the second man instantly dropped to his knees and begged for mercy, whimpering like a dog. Ali stabbed him several times and stood back, regaining his composure, realizing what he had done. There was no time to waste if he was to escape capture. He went through their possessions and transferred everything of value to a small bag. He then left the hotel.

It was nearly ten o'clock when a well-known England face, a Chelsea boy with a healthy domestic and international reputation, ducked in and passed the word along that .

everyone was mobbing up at the end of the street in a small square, boxed in by bars. The French were walking around attacking ones and twos, picking on football fans who had no interest in fighting, nicking their money and passports. There was a rumour going round that an Englishman's throat had been cut and that he had almost bled to death. The French were a couple of hundred yards from the square, and it was time to show these cunts who was boss. The bar emptied and a hundred-strong crew moved up the road in total silence. More England were waiting up ahead. Gary recognized various faces, the firm that had now come together mostly from London and the home counties, but with a few northerners in tow, plus Jesus and some Villa. In the square there was the usual hush, followed by movement towards one of five converging streets. It didn't take long to find the French. They were strutting along, the easy pickings and their numbers giving them a false sense of security. Without cameras or watching riot police, England went straight in and battered them, the narrowness of the street ensuring that the confrontation was full on and brutal. The English came out at the other end of the street and carried on running the French along a bigger road till they'd scattered into small groups and there was no chance of them re-forming and coming back for seconds.

Phil loved travelling, and football gave him the excuse to do something different with his holidays. Football meant he could spend his money rolling through Europe on rattling trains, sleeping in dodgy *pensions* and getting pissed in iffy bars instead of spending the usual two weeks in a Spanish high-rise being force-fed buffet breakfasts and shitty music. He'd been following England abroad for nearly ten years now and had visited the Vatican in Italy, Auschwitz in Poland and the Great Wall in China. Travel was Phil's education. He loved the uncertainty of catching a train to a foreign city without knowing what was going to happen there or who he was going to meet. There was always an edge, the English reputation going ahead of the travelling contingent, milked to the full by the local media. Being attacked by twenty men in a Marseille street hadn't been much fun, but he was feeling better now. They were one small part of the city, and didn't represent the peaceful majority. His head was throbbing, but it was nothing a couple of beers wouldn't sort out. The others were probably out caning it in some bar right now. He got up, attached his padlock to the door and left the hostel. Despite the kicking, Phil refused to be put off. He loved seeing different places, ducking away from the glare of the posh hotels he couldn't afford, losing himself in the streets and markets. He walked till he spotted a decent-looking bar, went inside and ordered. The barman was friendly, the prices reasonable and the customers everyday locals, old boys and middle-aged couples knocking back spirits and wine like no one's business, a few younger people tucking into plates of food. He could smell something cooking out back and realized he was hungry. The walls were covered in black-and-white photos and memorabilia, and he could imagine the Resistance sitting here more than half a century before, plotting the overthrow of the Nazis. Phil sat by the window and watched the people pass, the buzz of a late-night Mediterranean port creating its own special atmosphere. He ordered another drink and a cheese roll stuffed with tomatoes and olives. Fucking beautiful. The bar was earthy and wholesome, a different world from the street where he'd got a hiding. Gazing through the smudged window, Phil saw an ambulance stop outside, held up by a turning taxi. The light flashed, but the driver didn't seem in much of a hurry. An unmarked police car hurried in the opposite direction, siren blaring. The waiter was standing nearby and said that two men had been murdered in one of the big hotels. Phil nodded and ordered another drink, settled in for some much needed therapy. This was the life. Six beers later he spotted Gary and the others trooping up the road. He could tell they'd been in a row by the excitement in their faces and the lean of their walk. He went over to the door and called them over, the boys surprised to see him up and about but quickly filing in and ordering, filling Phil in on the details. It had been going off all night. That bollocks about Category Cs and official security measures was just that. Phil nodded and took it in. When the big stories were finished the waiter picked his moment, came over and leant in close, asked if they were interested in buying tickets for tomorrow's match. Phil and Gary controlled themselves, jumping inside but keeping straight faces. They followed the waiter to the far end of the counter where a boy sat on a stool, sipping a bottle of Coke and picking at a piece of cake. He had six tickets and was charging well under the odds, which suggested they'd been nicked. Phil and Gary didn't give a toss. If he wanted to unload them quickly, then they were happy to oblige. They didn't bother arguing over a few francs and paid the asking price. The waiter took a cut from the boy, who finished his Coke and left the bar, vanishing into the night. Gary laid the tickets on the table for inspection, and they were sniffed and kissed, then tucked away for safe keeping. Phil noticed that his headache had gone. They toasted the waiter and the tout, drank up and got another round in. Things were looking up.

Douglas Coupland

She Swallowed Her Pearls on the Day of the Revolution

Douglas Coupland is the author of numerous novels, including Generation X, Microserfs and Girlfriend in a Coma. In this piece on Santiago, Chile, he seeks to point out the complicit silence about Chile's past which underwrites its current economic boom. 'It's important to remember that this is a boom without any artistic or poetic soul because the government literally killed an entire generation of artists and poets. It's a country like Watership Down, where the rabbits live in luxury, but only at the price of

regularized, undiscussed slaughter.'

'Liz Taylor,' Marta says.

I say, 'Huh?'

'I said, "Liz Taylor", darling. It's from Spanish, *liste* – meaning, "let's go". It's a Santiago thing.'

'Very well then – Liz Taylor,' I say, and the cab driver says, 'Si.'

I stick my hand out of the window – hot and dry – and we pass a row of 1930s Moderne townhouses converted into computer company headquarters. Marta puckers her face; I think she's worried she was being too frivolous. 'Santiagoans are not "lite" people,' she informs me; our taxicab runs a red light. Marta's a Santiago matron and a friend of a friend, and she insists on going to lunch. She throws me a quick spell-check – 'Ell, eye, tee, ee' – to let me know that she, like many Santiagoans, has travelled extensively and is hip to the subtle nuances of other languages. Marta has a Chilean degree in metallurgical engineering but works in PR for a newly invading US food franchise. Her two kids live in New York and Bogotá, and her husband lives in Denver. Chile is the one remaining country on earth where divorce is illegal. She's studied ikebana in the same class as Dewey Sukarno and has 240,000 frequent-flyer points on American Airlines. She's got a 1969 flip hair-do, which is either extremely hip or extremely out of it, but if you know her, you know it's the former.

Our cab is bolting downtown for lunch. Alongside us rages the Andes-born Mapocho river, a chocolate-milk sluice that bisects Santiago. No Seine, this. The Río Mapocho is as wild as the landscape that contains this city that lies in the middle of this long, skinny nation crinkled on the Pacific coast like an old running-shoe lace.

Through the window I see a glassy, sun-baked, gridded city like one in southern California. Some smog. There are clouds high up in the distance but they're not clouds, they're Andean glaciers atop jagged lavender slopes. Across the river a massive green-glass building shaped like a cell phone stands sentinel above us. I close my eyes and continue to think of this city at the edge of the world and its darker secrets and its larger dreams. I see pigskin couches, German restaurants, copies of *¡Hola!* magazine and patches of desert scrub between countless apartment buildings. I see surveillance cameras, handmade signs saying *Silencio* and walls painted canary yellows, acid-greens, kandy-kane reds and polyvinyl blues. I see military statues on every other corner and streets named after dates of invasions and conquests and liberations.

We purr through Bellavista, a funky, colourful square mile of art deco, palms and bananas hemmed into a mountainside nook. I ask both Marta and the cab driver what sort of people live in this neighbourhood. 'Poets,' says the cab driver, making me wonder if he's mocking the place, but then Marta adds, 'Yes, darling, poets.' I'm amazed that both Marta and the cabbie have ventured opinions. This is rare here. Nobody offers opinions in Chile. Which restaurant is better? They're all good. Which route is more scenic? They're both beautiful. What do you think of the current political situation? Oh, look, a lovely little dove over there. This is Pablo Neruda's homeland; words go deeper here and can sting and can definitely kill. Voiced opinions are not necessarily good things to have.

We whirr past the strangely isolated Sheraton hotel, a lone black Miesian block on the edge of Bellavista and plunked against the side of San Cristóbal mountain. 'Linda Evangelista is staying there tonight,' Marta tells me. 'She's in town to attend a party.' A FedEx van passes us, and a sidewalk cluster of prosperous young business people chatters by. She adds, 'Everybody is less than one degree of separation from each other in this city. No privacy.'

The cab then jolts across the river and into Santiago's historic centre, built largely during the nitrate boom of the early twentieth century, a Spanish-colonial hybrid of Madrid and Brussels. David Bowie's 'Panic in Detroit' comes over the radio, and immigrants from the countryside try to sell us bags of corn at the stop-light for 1,000 pesos. A sign on a broad Latin-style boulevard reads 'Avenida Libertador General Bernardo O'Higgins'. ('Oh-Heegeenz.') On the older, sooty-ochre buildings I see tiny earthquake fissures and bullet holes from the Terror of 1973.

The cabbie asks me why I'm in Santiago and using a patois cobbled together from Mexican restaurant menus and Speedy Gonzales cartoons. I tell him I'm here on holiday. He mutters something I can't understand.

'He thinks you're crazy,' Marta tells me. 'Santiagoans can't believe you're visiting their city as a tourist. They think you've made a mistake.' In this vein I tell her that simple postcards are nearly impossible to find. As well as no insects and no litter, I'm also unable to find gaucho trinkets or llama ephemera.

'Are you here as a starting point to go fishing in the lake district?' the cabbie asks me.

'Nope.'

'Easter Island?'

'No.'

'Riding in the desert up north?'

'No.'

'Antarctica?'

'No.'

'The beaches an hour to the west?'

'No.'

He seems flummoxed. 'The wine-making region?'

'No.'

'*Que?*' He grunts.

'He thinks I'm with the CIA,' I say, and Marta's face stretches tight as armadillo hides on local bongo drums. *Faux pas*.

We stop. 'We're here,' Marta says.

Here is the Hotel Carrera, Santiago's grand-old-dame hotel with black-marble conquistador murals and a *magnifico* entrance-stairway. 'I've always had the sensation,' Marta says, 'that Richard Nixon's daughters are for ever on the brink of coming in the front doors wearing Adolfo sun-dresses while snapping Kodak Instamatics.' The taxi, one of the few bargains in this oddly expensive city, is paid, and we go inside, the air-conditioning and the decrease in light like cool feathers against our skin.

Now – here's what I know about this place, and also, here's what Marta knows I know – but we haven't discussed it out loud:

In 1973 Chile was doing OK. Whether through isolation or conviction or boredom or pique, they were the first country to ever elect a Marxist government, a coalition headed by Dr Salvador Allende, who promptly nationalized the nation's copper mines and had eyes on the phone company and the fruit-growers. Within months a Nixon/CIA-engineered coup installed a pro-US regime headed by Augusto Pinochet (known on local graffiti as 'PIN-8'). Untold thousands of citizens, mainly young people – creative types – were arrested, tortured and brutalized, many thousands of whom have never been heard from again. An entire generation of creativity and talent was erased.

To the rest of the world, this episode, along with, say, excellent white wines and December strawberries, has become perhaps the best-known fact about Chile, and this isn't unfair. It's impossible to look at Chilean society without the lens of politics. All of current life is coloured by it: students play ping-pong in university rooms that everybody knows were once used as torture chambers; housewives marvel at the grocery-store's abundance but wonder if it is linked to the neighbour's boy who vanished in '75; fathers receive foreign-currency bundles from anonymous addresses at the brand-new local Mailboxes Etc. franchise. It all goes back to 1973.

'What have you noticed about Santiagoans?' Marta asks me. We're on the roof of the Carrera by the swimming pool, and the city is splayed around us like a Tinkertoy fantasia. Seersuckered executives lunching with each other and with ripe young nieces and nephews surround us. The feeling is retro and decadent, and I expect microphones in the salad.

I tell Marta I've noticed a lack of label-consciousness in the crowds I've seen – at the outdoor markets and in the thronging arcades and malls and bistros. 'An affirming lack of need to base one's sense of identity and purpose on Calvin Klein or the Chicago Bulls.'

'But no short pants.'

I laugh: 'No.' I'm wearing a pair of Banana Republic walking-shorts and have spent the morning being whistled at from cars, having old men mutter at me and children follow me on the brink of stoning me.

'Chile's culture is unchangeably macho,' Marta says, 'and if you're a boy and you wear khaki walking-shorts around town you might as well be wearing a comfortable, well-matched Liz Claiborne jacket and dress. Santiagoans will tell you that they're very modern about the wearing of walking-shorts but then they've never actually worn them around town themselves.' Marta bites an ice cube and frowns. 'Truth be told, Chileans have a huge problem with gentlemen in walking-shorts, period. Enough said. But what else – what have you noticed?'

Images spring to mind: 'A complete absence of luxury cars.'

'Who wants to be kidnapped? Besides, luxury is considered a bit vulgar and sexually dirty here. There's the old joke about Santiagoans: if you want to flaunt your wealth and buy a second car, just make sure it's the same make, model and colour as your first car. And besides, most people own a few cars to get around the odd day/even day anti-smog restrictions. Like Mexico City.'

We order coffee. The Philip Johnson AT&T-clone building beside the hotel looks like Barbie's First Skyscraper. 'What cities does Santiago remind you of?' Marta asks.

'Mexico City.'

'Where else? Make a list.'

'I'll do better than make a list. I'll add percentages:

'19% Mexico City
 18% Orange County, California
 17% Barcelona
  8% Westwood, Los Angeles
  7% Capetown
  7% Hamburg
  6% Madrid
  4% Bermuda
  3% Portland, Oregon
  3% Denver.'

'That's only 92 per cent.'

'How did you add that up so quickly?' I ask.

'My engineering degree, darling. And you're still 8 per cent short.'

'OK. 8 per cent Miami.'

'Perfect.'

Beef arrives at the table; lunch has begun. ('Beef beef beef beef beef. We like our red meat here, darling, yes we do.') We eat lunch and chat about local-steel plaza sculptures and the strangely large number of young people lugging violins, guitars and violas within the city's spotlessly delightful subway system. I also note that the local economy is tightly bound to that of Asia: Hyundai, Samsung and Daewoo Heavy Industries logos abound. 'God help the Korean won.'

Marta's cell phone rings. Everybody in this city seems to have cell phone. Chile has the world's first fully digitized phone system and competition has made prices plunge.

Calls to Europe connect the moment the final number is dialled. Regardless, Chile is far enough away from the rest of the world that a phone call from there still has the frisson of genuine distance.

'My sister,' she says. 'Excuse me.' Marta's sister is at the Termas de Callquenes baths in the south. 'Charles Darwin loved it there,' I'm told when she hangs up. 'Now – where were we?'

'I can't remember,' I say, and we look over at the Andes, known locally as the Cordillera. The smog is vanishing, and Santiago is becoming more visible, shivering and shimmering from nearly two decades of solid, unimpeded economic growth. It's the richest, cleanest city in South America and it shows: five million people who all just stepped out of the shower to put on brand-new crisp white shirts with the fold-lines still warped across their chests. And when they walk out their doors, it's into a city that appears to have been built ten minutes ago.

'You know what?' I say. 'There's almost nothing old here. And the city, it seems – convulsed with money. I was expecting, well – I was expecting a banana republic.'

'I know what you mean,' Marta says. 'Santiagoans are like jackpot lottery winners. Our phones ring non-stop. We suddenly have relatives creeping out of all woodworks; we have countless new friends we never knew we had. We're like Seoul, Taipei and Kuala Lumpur. The government only wants quick development. It's unwilling or unable to regulate changes. Old neighbourhoods vanish overnight to make way for condos. People here say they like the glamour of all this change, but what they really like is all the shininess of it all.' A helicopter cuts conversation dead for a few seconds. 'And we finally got real-estate hyperinflation. Aren't we up to date? Come on – let's go have a look at the view. Liz Taylor.'

Ten storeys below us is the Plaza de la Constitución – wide and empty like Red Square minus a Kremlin – and the heavily guarded Palacio de la Moneda, the seat of government. To the north a few miles sits Mount San Cristóbal with its

funicular and gondola and the Bosque Norte, a mini Wall
Street neighbourhood with a cluster of chrome Moulinex-
appliance-type buildings that bespeaks the recent Klondike of
foreign investment.

'I know what you're thinking,' Marta says.

'Tell me, then.'

'You're thinking of plutocrats standing up here watching
the revolution through hunting binoculars. Tiaras falling from
heads and scraping the rioting college students below.
Anarchists stuffing bombs inside the baked Alaska.'

'Yes and no. OK, then – yes.'

'But it's not that colourful any more. You know that, don't
you?'

I think of the cliché tattered angry red political posters of
yore. Long gone – replaced by sterile backlit Plexi signs atop
burgeoning glass towers touting BellSouth, Compaq, Nestlé,
IBM, Xerox and Citicorp. 'I do.'

There's something Marta wants to tell me, but she's
hesitating, even though I'm a foreigner and I'll be gone soon.

Here's what I know Marta's thinking – somewhere beneath
the Anne Klein dress and the Zegna sunglasses – things I
know because I spoke with her daughter, Linda, in Berkeley
the week before:

'. . . Mom thinks citizens are superstitious and afraid of
making any political changes because the economy might be
hurt.

'. . . Mom thinks citizens have been handsomely paid to
erase their memories.

'. . . Mom thinks that fifteen years of unparalleled growth
have rendered citizens unable to select between good and
bad. They are unwilling and/or unable to believe in the
process of democracy.'

'Linda, how can you go on like this?' I had asked. 'How
can you pull so much politics out of a bag like that?'

'You grow up in it in Santiago. You spend your life waiting
for a toxic cloud – a warning on the TV or radio that tells you

the worst has happened – that the end is on its way. Santiago's the most political place on earth. There are bones of graduate students cemented into buildings – or it feels that way. A female student was set on fire as recently as July 1986. But Mom'd sooner die than tell you. But it's all bottled up inside her,' Linda told me. 'She's had her public mouth bolted shut since 1970.'

Back on the hotel roof I'm prattling. I mention the local McDonald's and toy product tie-ins with the simultaneous US/Chile release of Disney's *Flubber*. Marta sends me a queasy shiver, like she's caught me masturbating. 'There's nothing quite so American as the sight of two corporations fucking, is there, darling?'

I fall into a dream, like some screwed-up 1970s movie. Spanish and sexy and sleek, yet botched and in pain: Faye Dunaway imprisoned for decades to starve inside a chromed living room; schizophrenic businessmen cannibalizing each other and hanging what bones remain on the thousands of cell phone antennae across the city. These aren't the pictures I expected to see here. I wanted to see a sexy salsa-loving pineapple-scented culture – and that's all here, too – but there's an exotic dangerous film on top, and it comes from some other world.

'No. I guess not,' I say.

'Pardon my French.' She blushes. 'What came over me? C'mon,' she adds. 'Let's check out the antique market by Plaza Brasil. Liz Taylor.'

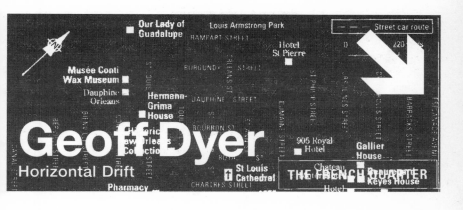

Geoff Dyer

Horizontal Drift

Geoff Dyer is the author of three novels: Paris Trance, The Search, The Colour of Memory; a critical study of John Berger, Ways of Telling; and three genre-defying titles, But Beautiful (winner of the 1992 Somerset Maugham Prize, short-listed for the Mail on Sunday/John Llewellyn Rhys Memorial Prize), The Missing of the Somme and Out of Sheer

Rage.

In 1991 I lived for a while in New Orleans, in an apartment on Esplanade, just beyond the French Quarter where, from time to time, British tourists are murdered for refusing to hand over their video cameras to the cracked-out muggers who live and work nearby. I never had any trouble – possibly because I have never owned a video camera – even though I walked everywhere at all times.

I had decided to come to New Orleans after a girlfriend and I passed through, on our way to Los Angeles from New York. We were delivering a car and though, usually, you are allowed only a few hundred miles more than it takes to drive cross-continent in a straight line, our car's original mileage had not been recorded, and so we zigzagged our way across the States, exceeding the normal distance by several thousand miles and thoroughly exhausting ourselves in the process. In the course of this frenzied itinerary we'd stayed only one night in New Orleans, but it – by which I mean the French Quarter rather than the city at large – seemed like the most perfect place in the world, and I vowed that, when I next had a chunk of free time, I would return. I make such vows all the time without keeping them but on this occasion, a year after first visiting, I returned to New Orleans to live for three months.

I spent the first few nights in the Rue Royal Inn while I looked for an apartment to rent. I hoped to find a place in the heart of the Quarter, somewhere with a balcony and rocking chairs and wind chimes, overlooking other places with rocking chairs and balconies, but I ended up on the dangerous fringes of the Quarter, in a place with a tiny balcony overlooking a vacant lot which seethed with unspecified threat as I walked home at night.

The only people I knew in New Orleans were James and
Ian, a gay couple in their fifties, friends of an acquaintance of
a woman who worked for my publisher in England. They
were extremely hospitable, but because they were a good
deal older than me and because they both had AIDS and
liked to live quietly, I quickly settled into a routine of work and
solitude. In films, whenever a man moves to a new town –
even if he has served a long jail term for murdering his wife –
he very soon meets a woman at the check-out of the local
supermarket or the diner where he has his first breakfast. I
spent much of my thirties moving to new towns, towns where
I knew no one, and I never met a woman in the supermarket,
or the Croissant d'Or where I had breakfast on my first
morning in New Orleans. Even though I did not meet a
waitress at the aptly named Croissant d'Or, I continued to
have breakfast there every day because, in my opinion,
they serve the best almond croissants in the world. Some
days it rained for days on end, the heaviest rain I had ever
seen, but however hard it was raining I never missed my
breakfast at the Croissant d'Or, partly because of the
excellence of the croissants and coffee, but mainly because
going there became part of the habitual rhythm of my
working day.

In the evenings I went to the bar across the road, the Port
of Call, where I tried, unsuccessfully, to engage the barmaid
in conversation, and watched the Gulf War on CNN. On the
night of the first air strikes against Baghdad the bar was
rowdy with excitement and foreboding. Yellow ribbons were
tied around many of the trees on Esplanade which I walked
up every day on my way to the Croissant d'Or where, as I ate
my almond croissants, I liked to read the latest reports from
the Gulf, either in the *New York Times* or the local paper, the
name of which – the Louisiana Something? – I have
forgotten. After breakfast I walked home and worked for as
long as I could and then strolled through the Quarter, led on,
it seemed, by the sound of wind chimes, which hung from
almost every building. It was January, but the weather was

mild, and I often sat by the Mississippi, reading about New
Orleans and its history. Because the city was located at the
mouth of the river, its foundations were in mud and each year
the buildings sank more deeply into it. As well as being
warped by the sun and rotted by rain and humidity many
buildings in the Quarter sloped markedly as a result of
subsidence. This straying from the vertical was
complemented by a horizontal drift. The volume of detritus
carried south by the Mississippi was such that the river was
silting itself up and changing course so that, effectively, the
city was moving. Every year the streets moved a couple of
inches in relation to the river, subtly altering the geography of
the town. Decatur Street, for example, where James and Ian
lived, had moved several degrees from the position recorded
on nineteenth-century maps.

As I sat there one afternoon, by the Mississippi, a freight
rumbled past on the railroad track behind me, moving very
slowly. I had always wanted to hop a freight and I sprang up,
trying to muster up the courage to leap aboard. The length of
the train and its slow speed meant that I had a long time –
too long – to contemplate hauling myself aboard, but I was
frightened of getting into trouble or injuring myself and so I
stood there for five minutes, watching the box cars clank past
until, finally, there were no more cars and the train had
passed. Watching it curve out of sight I was filled with a
magnolia-tinted regret, the kind of feeling you get when you
see a woman in the street, when your eyes meet for a
moment but you make no effort to speak to her, and then
she is gone and you spend the rest of the day thinking that,
had you spoken, she would have been pleased, not
offended, and you would, perhaps, have fallen in love with
each other. You wonder what her name might have been.
Angela, perhaps. Instead of hopping the freight, I went back
to my apartment on Esplanade and had the character in the
novel I was working on do so.

When you are lonely, writing can keep you company. It is
also a form of self-compensation, a way of making up for

things – as opposed to making things up – that did not quite
happen.

As the eventless weeks went by it became warmer and
more humid and Mardi Gras drew near. A condition of renting
my apartment was that I move out during Mardi Gras, when
the landlord charged four or five times the normal weekly
rate. Fortunately, James and Ian were going away and they
allowed me to stay in their place on Decatur, which was no
longer quite as close to the river as it had once been.

At first it was fun, Mardi Gras. I liked the sport of trying to
catch stuff – plastic beakers, beads and other trinkets:
rubbish, really – thrown from the crazy floats inching through
the crazy streets. It was like a cross between basketball and
being in a mob of crazed refugees scrambling for food rations
thrown by soldiers. I really got into it. Being tall, I could
outreach most people even though there are some tall men,
mainly black, in Louisiana; the whites are shorter for the most
part, easy to out-jump.

One evening I was part of a herd buffaloing along Rampart,
leaping for beakers and beads, when gun shots were heard.
Suddenly everyone was screaming and running in panic.
Then there were sirens and police everywhere and things
returned to the normal Mardi Gras uproar.

As the carnival progressed so it became more unpleasant,
almost a bore. The Quarter was jammed with college kids
and tins of Budweiser and broken plastic beakers, and the
streets reeked of beery vomit. The flip side of this were the
balls organized by various krewes. Ian had given me his
invitation to one of these bashes, where I met Angela, a
young black woman who was studying wealth accumulation
at Law School.

The day after the ball she came round to James and Ian's
apartment wearing freshly laundered Levi's and a red blouse.
Her hair was tied back in a ribbon, also red. We stood side by
side on the balcony, drinking white wine in glasses so fine
you hardly dared hold them. Our hands on the balcony rail
were only inches apart. I moved my hand until it almost

touched hers and then it was touching hers, and she didn't move her hand away so I stroked her arm.

'That feels nice,' she said, still looking out into the street. Then we kissed, each holding a delicate glass behind the other's back. Unsure what to do when we had finished kissing we kissed some more.

Shortly after Mardi Gras, when the Quarter had returned to its normal, empty state, Donovan, a guy about my age and height, moved into the apartment next to mine. He had longish hair, dressed less smartly – T-shirt, baseball shoes – than I did at that time. We met on the stairs a couple of times, compared apartments – they were almost identical – went for a burger at the Port of Call and generally started hanging out together. About four years previously – 'April Fool's Day 1987,' he said – Donovan had been told he had skin cancer. The doctors gave him only a 30/70 chance of living but he had come through a series of operations sufficiently full of life to try, five months before we met, to kill himself. Since then he'd been in a mental home in LA and was now 'undergoing' further cancer treatment at Tulane (hospitals, in Donovan's resumé, played the part of colleges in mine).

Being from California, Donovan was a good tennis player, and in the afternoons we often knocked up for an hour (he couldn't see the point in keeping score). He was a much better player than me, but since I enjoyed running down every ball and was possessed of a fierce determination to win (even though we weren't scoring), we were perfectly matched. When he took off his sweat-soaked T-shirt at the end of our first game I was shocked by the state of his back and chest, by the scarred and maimed flesh. In the evenings we got stoned or hung out in bars, usually the Port of Call, sometimes other places. He was always happy to talk about 'the cancer and shit' he'd been through. He'd been living at his parents' house when the first test results came back positive.

'I was in the bathroom, shaving. My mom opened the

envelope and came in and hugged me. I'm like, "Mom, I'm *shaving.*" '

'You were never upset?'

'It was a drag. It fucked up my life but I wasn't upset. You know, they kept talking about "undergoing" surgery, "undergoing" chemo. It really bugged me. I never saw it like that. I was just living my life. I wasn't like "undergoing" it.'

'So why'd you try to kill yourself?'

'It wasn't like I was depressed or anything. I didn't even want to die particularly. I just didn't want to live any more.'

He'd been doing coke all night, he said. Then he sat in his car drinking beer, playing tapes, quite happy, a tube from the exhaust filling the interior with carbon monoxide.

We were sitting on my balcony, stoned, when he told me this, watching kids playing in the vacant lot. Twilight was falling.

'What did your friends think?'

'I think they thought, "That's just like Donovan." '

The doctors at the mental home were no less intrigued than I was. They had encountered many attempted suicides but had never come across a case like his. Searching for clues, they asked if he was 'possibly an alcoholic?'

'I should hope so,' he said. 'After all the time, money and effort I've put into it.' Nothing made any difference to him. He didn't care about anything and yet, at the same time, he had a great capacity for friendship. He was thoughtful, generous (he wasn't working but he always had plenty of money), never imposing, but eager to come along whenever I suggested we go for a drink or something to eat. If ever I knocked on his door he was always lying on his bed, drinking beer or watching TV. He never read anything – not even newspapers – and he was never bored. He spent all his time being himself, being American, being Donovan.

It was dark now, still warm. We could no longer see the kids playing, but we could hear their voices.

On a weekend when Donovan's family were visiting, Angela and I drove to Mississippi in her car. She had been away for a time, staying with friends on the east coast, and we had not seen each other for several weeks. Also, although we had necked a good deal we had never quite slept together. I hoped that would happen in the course of what I referred to as our 'freedom ride'. Angela did not know what I meant. This was eight years ago; back then I was often surprised by how much people didn't know. That's one of the things about travelling, one of the things you learn: many people in the world, even educated ones, don't know much, and it doesn't actually matter at all.

We drove through the flatness of Louisiana, past Walker Evans scenery and lots of poor housing, which became poorer as we got into Mississippi. If we were driving slowly people stopped what they were doing – even if they were doing nothing – and watched us pass. The sky was heavy and wet, silted with cloud. I was vaguely hoping that we would be subjected to racial abuse, that a redneck would throw a brick through the windshield of our car, but everyone we met – gas-pump attendants, mainly – seemed too worn out and courteous to notice anything except the make of car we were driving.

We checked into a motel in Jackson and ate at a diner with neon in the windows, where they served large portions of home-cooked food. After dinner we went back to the motel. I had forgotten to bring the condoms I had bought in New Orleans but by the time that became evident we were both too turned on to care.

'If you've got AIDS I'll kill you,' Angela said, guiding me into her. When we had finished having sex, we lay in the almost-darkness of Mississippi, car lights raking the ceiling, hearing the TV from the room next door.

'Have you ever been with a black girl before?'

'Yes.'

'How many?' she said, sounding relieved.

'Two. And you know the funny thing?'

'What?'

'They both asked me if I'd ever been with a black girl before.'

We had bought beer from a liquor store and spent the rest of the evening drinking in our room, like we had robbed a gas station and were on the run.

Back in New Orleans, Donovan and I also went on excursions, out into the swamps – the things floating in the water like wood that had been drifting for thousands of years turned out to be alligators – or driving aimlessly around the city, listening to rock tapes. One night we were driving on Filmore, just east of the City Park. It was raining slightly. The wipers smeared blurs of red across the windshield. Neon lay in green puddles. A car was waiting on lights up ahead and we drifted into it. We were not going fast but there was a loud noise of metal, a brief drizzle of glass. Two black guys got out and walked back towards us. Donovan reached for the glove compartment, began opening it. The guys checked out their beat-up station-wagon, looking for damage. There was none, or at least there was no *new* damage, and they didn't seem too bothered. Donovan shut the glove compartment and wound down the window. One of the guys came over to talk with him. When he smelt the smell of grass in our car he started laughing, and Donovan handed him the joint he had been smoking. Then the two guys got back in their car and drove off.

For a moment I had been extremely nervous. In America you are conscious of the race thing in a way that you never are in England. You find yourself in a black neighbourhood and you think, 'Shit, I'm in a black neighbourhood, maybe I shouldn't be here.' Donovan said he'd been a little uneasy too, when they first got out of the car.

'That's why I carry this,' he said, opening the glove compartment again and reaching inside. He passed me a gun. I had never held a gun before. It was small, heavy, black and dangerous-looking. I handed it back to Donovan, who put it back in the glove compartment.

'Trouble is, I've only got two bullets left. It's like, what am I going to do if three guys try to fuck with me?'

'Shoot one of them and then shoot yourself?'

'Two bullets,' said Donovan, shaking his head.

'Maybe you should buy some more bullets.'

'You're right, dude. I've got to buy some more bullets.'

'Two bullets . . .'

'Shit, two bullets is like nothing.'

'What use is a gun with only two bullets?'

'A gun needs six bullets.'

'As in six-shooter.'

'Basically, I'm four bullets short.'

'You're working at thirty-three per cent of your potential capacity.'

'Six minus four equals two.'

'A shortfall of four.'

'A guy with only two bullets in his gun is a fucking pussy.'

'I didn't want to say it. I thought you might be offended.'

'Even though you didn't say it, I knew that's what you were thinking.'

'If I were you I'd go to the bullet shop tomorrow. First thing.'

'You know what I'm gonna do when I get there?'

'You're going to buy four bullets.'

'I might even buy six.'

'Good idea.'

'Then I'd have two spare.'

'Two spare, exactly.'

We parked the car outside our building and walked quickly – it was raining harder now – to the Port of Call. The Gulf War was over and it was rowdier than ever. Donovan had slept with the barmaid, the one I had tried to engage in conversation, and she let us have free drinks. I was hungry and ordered a burger; Donovan had already eaten dinner but he wanted one too. We'd been stoned before; now, with the drinking, we were getting fucked up. He told me about his time in the military. He had been stationed in Berlin, where he and a buddy had sold classified information to the Soviets on a regular basis. As a result they'd ended up with so much cash they were hard pressed to spend it. They'd fly to Paris for the weekend, paying a thousand bucks a night for beautiful French hookers. He'd also started making headway with the coke habit which had gotten out of control in LA.

'Did you feel bad about it?'

'Blowing all that money on coke and whores?'

'No. Selling secrets to MI5 – I mean, the KGB.'

'It just felt like easy money.'

'It sounds like treason to me.'

'Well it *was*, dude.'

Strange: here he was telling me about his treasonous untrustworthiness, but it never occurred to me not to trust him, not to believe stuff he told me. And not just that: in his way he seemed one of the most trustworthy people I had ever met, someone I could entrust things to – not that I *had* anything to entrust him with – without any fear of betrayal.

All this means, I suppose, is that he was my friend. Living as I have, in different cities, in different countries, I've got used to making new friends at an age when many people are living off the diminishing stockpile amassed at university, when they were nineteen or twenty. It's one of the things about the way I've lived that has made me happiest, and maybe the only purpose of this story – this non-story – is to record the simple fact that, in New Orleans, a town where we knew hardly anyone, Donovan and I became friends.

'You know, I'm still thinking about those bullets,' he said after we had finished our burgers and ordered more beer.

'I knew it,' I said. 'I could tell.'

'I could buy ten: four and six.'

'Two sets of six.'

'But I don't need that many.'

'So stick to six. I mean, *buy* six.'

'Two plus four.'

'Equals six.'

'Plus two left over.'

'Bingo!'

My time in New Orleans was drawing to an end. To go on with the book I was writing I needed to be in California for a while. Just as I was getting a life it was time to leave.

Angela and I slept together a few more times after we got back from our freedom ride, but there was nothing happening really. We had seen each other so infrequently that the transition from seeing each other to not seeing each other was almost imperceptible. Perhaps I had begun to pick up some of Donovan's indifference to the way things turn out. Also I began to wonder if I was not feeling quite right: a slight burning, very slight, when I pissed.

Donovan was thinking of going west too, but not *too* far west. If he ended up in LA again, he was sure he would kill himself. He was thinking of Las Vegas, which was 'west of New Orleans but not as far west as LA'.

'Right,' I said. 'Exactly.' He had friends there, in Vegas. From time to time we spoke of my collaborating with him on a book about his life. 'All the espionage shit' gave such a book considerable commercial potential, but I saw it as a kind of parable, one without any lesson or moral, from which it would be impossible to learn anything or draw any conclusions. I was keen to do it and so was he.

The night before I left we got stoned and sat by the Mississippi (allegedly an unwise thing to do after dark). The moon was almost full. Strictly speaking, it was not a full moon but it was full enough. I told Donovan about the freight I wished I'd hopped.

'You should have done it, dude,' he said.

'I know. I wrote about it instead.'

'That night I tried to kill myself, I almost didn't go ahead with it. I could hardly be bothered. Then I thought, "What the fuck, you can sit here in your car drinking any night. Like c'mon, let's get on with it." '

'What will power.'

Tankers went by, full of slow purpose, between us and the cranes of Algiers Point across the water. There was no fog, but the sound of foghorns is a part of my memory of the scene. Every now and again the fullish moon was obscured by clouds making their way to the sea. The river did not seem like a strong brown god; it just seemed like a huge river, so old and heavy it had long ago lost all interest in making it to the Gulf of Mexico or wherever. Only the weight of implacable habit impelled it onwards.

The following morning Donovan drove me to the airport, and I flew to San Francisco and took a bus to Santa Cruz. The burning sensation I felt when pissing had become unignorable. I went to a clinic where they gave me antibiotics for chlamydia. Donovan and I spoke on the phone from time to time but our plans to do a book together came to nothing: the novel I was writing took longer to complete than I had hoped and I could not look beyond that. Gradually we lost touch.

I heard from a friend recently that James and Ian had both died. The last I heard of Donovan, he was living in Las Vegas. When I tried to call him several years ago the number was unavailable. I had no fall-back address for him – this was in the days before e-mail – and have no idea where he is. I have moved many times since New Orleans and do not know if Donovan has tried to get in touch with me. From time to time I have thought about trying to track him down, but have no idea how to go about it. He could be in LA, he could be anywhere. Chances are, he has blown his brains out by now.

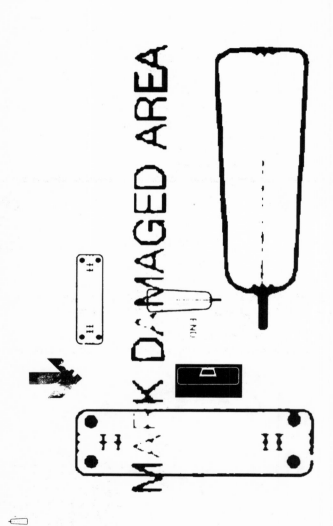

MARK DAMAGED AREA

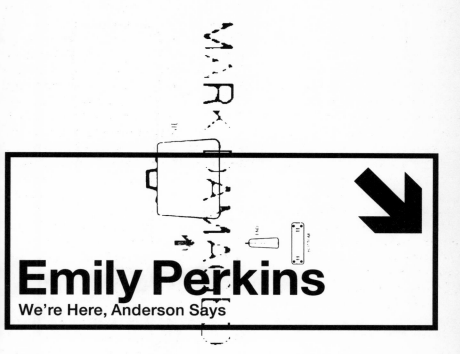

Emily Perkins

We're Here, Anderson Says

Emily Perkins was born in New Zealand in 1970 and has lived in London since 1994. She has published a collection of short stories, Not Her Real Name (winner of the 1997 Geoffrey Faber Memorial Prize) and a novel, Leave Before You Go (both Picador). Her stories have been widely anthologized and she is at work on a second novel. She has done some travelling but would like to do

more.

We're here, Anderson says, to see if our relationship is beyond repair. Or – as he professes to hope – if we can restore it. If it is retrievable. Anderson has taken a liking to R words. 'Our relationship may just be retrievable, Angie, and I for one would like to give it a try.' Even though he said it in his fake-sincere American accent, trying to take the vulnerability out of the words, I couldn't help but see Anderson as a lolloping dog, golden and eager, snuffling to pick up our relationship between his friendly jaws, from wherever it was I'd thrown it. I told Jane that and she laughed, but I could tell she thought I was mean and hard. Jane is terminally single, so what she thinks doesn't exactly count.

In reality Anderson looks nothing like a dog. He's more a cat person, which is one of the things that drew me to him. He has almond-shaped eyes and sinewy arms and sleek black hair which he may well be losing. He is losing. When I wake up in the mornings one of the first things I do is brush the pillow free of his fallen-out hairs. He is losing it from the front and also from the crown of his head. Unusually for me, I am still with Anderson. Normally, at the first sign of trouble or evidence of fallibility, I am running as fast as my little legs can carry me. 'Better no relationship than a bad relationship' has been something I liked to say. But with Anderson it has seemed as though it might be all right to sort through the bad stuff, to try and see the whole. To love anyway. The fact that I am tipping thirty doubtless has something to do with all of this. Tick tick.

Anyway, things haven't been so hot lately. Anderson suspects this is my fault; I am convinced it is his. An example of our discontent would be that my habit of littering, while previously unnoticed or ignored, has now become the focal

point for everything that is wrong with modern society. I
exemplify contemporary apathy, Anderson says. I remain
infantilized in my relationships with authority, I fear
government, I will never be capable of effecting real change.
Change for what, I say, and Change for the good, he replies.
It's an empty crisp packet, I say, not a fucking ballot slip.
Anderson can be pompous but it isn't his fault. His mother
was a famous sixties figure – he was brought up on a diet of
communal marijuana and indigestible bread. Once we went
round to visit and Anderson's mother's boyfriend was putting
lentils through the juicer. Anderson is, obviously, Anderson's
last name. His first name is unrepeatable.

The littering thing is just one item in a list of complaints
Anderson has about me. My theory is that he thinks he wants
to improve me, but secretly he is drawn to the fact that I do
not care. Whatever (I am trying to curb my inclination to
over-analyse everything), his confusion results is a consistent
tone of disapproval. In turn I become unconfident, then
depressed, and then I rebel. This cycle can take place two or
three times in an afternoon. I play the old songs a lot,
especially when I am trying to behave against type, by
cleaning the house.

It was Anderson's idea to come away. I am grateful for it –
he has made all the arrangements. He looked through
brochures, he enquired about hotels, he found cheap flights.
Neither of us has been on a holiday like this before, where all
there is to do is lie around in the sunshine and relax.
Anderson's holidays, a legacy from his mother, usually involve
Third World countries, disadvantaged locals and potential-
for-trade investigations, or walks in the rain in Wales. I am
more of a city-break person, preferring coffee bars, art
galleries and shopping to the delights of the elements. But I
am quite enjoying doing as I'm told.

We're here now, Anderson says. We had to get up at
two-thirty this morning to be at the airport in time for
check-in. I look like my passport photograph. We walk

blinking off the plane but heat doesn't rush at us the way I
had imagined it would. The other people from our flight look
different from us. We stand cramped in a little oblong bus
with controls at both ends and I try not to mind that they look
different from us. If I were to mention this to a certain person,
he would tell me I was an inveterate snob. Anderson truly
believes we are all equal, even those with bad dress sense. I
think his egalitarianism is rare. A lot of people pretend to
believe this but, generally, if you scratch the surface, they
don't want their kids going to playgroup with those other,
allegedly equal kids. I know this is not an earth-shattering
insight into human nature but I find it reassuring nevertheless.
It means I'm not alone. But I love Anderson's goodness, even
when it bugs me, like now, that if I were to point out the
preponderance of shell suits and gold chains on this bus, he
wouldn't laugh.

The hotel is much nicer than I expected. Like me, it
matches its photograph. Despite Anderson's investigations
I'd been convinced that the image in the glossy brochure was
a lie and we would arrive to find a building site with ants on
the benches and rusty water. Instead we are in a creamy
concreted apartment with crimson bougainvillaea running
down the sides of our balcony walls. The hotel storeys are
tiered, so though we're on the first floor, we look out over a
small garden towards the pool. We dump our suitcases
unopened on the double bed and run down the stairs to the
beach.

Some people set a lot of store by horizons. Personally, I
think they're all the same. So I let Anderson walk on the
water side, getting a crick in his neck from staring out
through his sunglasses at the barely distinguishable line
between sky and sea. There are waves, and the sand is
coarse and yellow. We walk on the wet sand past rows of
black-and-orange striped deck-chairs. We're walking
towards a rock-covered curve in the beach. We can't see
what's beyond it. It's warm, but not hot. I had thought it
would be hot. The lines of deck-chairs have ended and a

wind picks up. It blows darts of dry sand at our legs. I sing
some lines from a Joni Mitchell song. Anderson pushes me
because if there's one thing he doesn't like about his mother
it's the music of her generation. His mother claims an
erstwhile acquaintance with Joni Mitchell. For a woman
whose life has been devoted to the belief that everybody is
equal, she has a great respect for the famous and invokes
the names of celebrities she has met as often as possible.
That Anderson hates hippie music is one of the things that I
like about him.

I'm singing the song a bit and when I run out of words I
remember I start talking. 'It's so beautiful,' I say, 'look at
those hotels down there, look at those houses, it's like how I
imagine California.' We take off our sandals and, holding
them, walk in the shallows so that the sand doesn't keep
stinging our legs. 'Aren't those pink flowers amazing? Did you
see that enormous cactus at the airport? I never imagined
them to look so extraordinary, it was much better than a
photograph.' I don't know if Anderson is listening, but I keep
talking because there's a scared, thrown-overboard feeling in
my stomach that I'm trying not to think about. 'The water's
so warm. Do you think it's very polluted?' This last one, I
expect, will get a response from Anderson, but before he
answers there's a big grinding noise and an aeroplane
appears from nowhere, vast in the massive sky.

The plane, with its shark-grey underneath, swings over us
and on towards the airport just north of the beach. It's a
wonderful sight, romantic and modern. I feel happier.
Anderson doesn't say anything.

Later, back in our room, we put on our swimsuits and laugh
at each other. Our bodies are frightened and white. Anderson
tries out the snorkel gear he has brought with him. He fits the
mask tight over his face so that the skin bulges slightly on the
outside of it. Then he squeezes the breathing pipe under the
mask strap and tucks the mouthpiece into his mouth. I laugh
in the spirit of us laughing at each other in our swimsuits, but

inwardly I am cringing. Anderson walks slowly around the beige room motioning with his hands as if he's doing breast-stroke. Then he raises first one arm, then the other, dancing sixties style. Now he's doing the Mash, and that dance with the gestures like hitchhiking. I despair of Anderson. What will he look like, down at the pool?

I shouldn't worry. The poolside is not an intimidatingly fashionable spot. Most of the people are in family groups, couples with matching short flicky haircuts, garish T-shirts and young children. The pool itself is a pleasing organic shape, in keeping with the seventies style of the hotel. We find two blue sun-loungers and settle in with our towels, our tanning lotion and our books. Anderson's snorkel and mask lie under his sun-lounger like a small parcel of kelp. He isn't going to use them in the pool, he assures me, but maybe if he walks through the gate in the fence and across the road to the beach. I am trying to love Anderson but the effort of it is making me a bit weepy. I lie with my eyes shut and try not to feel dislocated, here on this remote island, cut off and alone. Eventually, to the soft sound of waves on the beach behind me, I fall asleep.

We're not here, Anderson says, to spend all our time apart from each other. He says this when, back in the room, I want to go downstairs for a drink and he wants to lie down. I know what 'lie down' means.

'Who spent all this afternoon apart from me,' I say, 'at the beach? You did.'

'Or, equally, you spent it apart from me at the pool,' he answers.

'We were at the pool first. It was your choice to separate off and go to the beach.' I don't know why I'm saying this. I could care less that he spent the afternoon at the beach.

'And it was your choice not to come with me.'

'I was asleep.' I sense a new tack. 'Which is why I don't feel like lying down now. If you're tired after snorkelling, why don't you have a nap and meet me in the bar later?'

'Ange. Angel.' He touches my arm. The feeling of his hand tingles. 'Come on. We're on holiday.'

It occurs to me that I should never have come on a holiday paid for by somebody else.

'All right,' I say. 'Just for a minute.'

Dinner looks like it will be a success. There's a little restaurant on the beach-front, past the rocks we walked to today. We sit under the striped awning and wrangle with large plates of seafood. When I met Anderson he was a vegetarian, but that didn't last. I used to cook breakfasts on weekend mornings, and I'm afraid he fell, unoriginally, for the temptations of sizzling bacon. At the time I enjoyed knowing that there were limits to Anderson's self-control. Now I'm not sure. Here at the restaurant, our langoustines are like something from a bad acid-trip, with giant claws and long plated bodies. 'Imagine one of those on your pillow,' I say, and Anderson winces. He's going brown already. His mother has olive skin, and he tans easily. It's nice to see him across the table, by the candle with the red glass surround protecting it.

'Where are you?' Anderson says. The truth is, I am preoccupied with work. Just because you go somewhere new, it doesn't mean you can instantly adapt. Everything that happened yesterday still only happened yesterday, even though we're now in a different time zone.

'You know, Harold is really out of order,' I say.

'Who?' Anderson's head twitches slightly, as if to look around for someone behind him. His prawns are all peeled, the shells to one side of his plate, the fleshy insides lying there naked and ready. I am eating mine as I go, and getting prawn juice all over my hands.

'Harold. The unit manager. He's a jerk. Yesterday he sent round –.'

'Angie. Forget about it. We're supposed to be thinking about us.'

I can't believe those words just came out of Anderson's mouth. 'You sound as if you're in a soap opera.'

'Don't be a bitch.'

'Don't call me a bitch.'

On the way home we walk past a souvenir shop that is just closing up. There are racks of tea towels with maps of the islands on them, and a wall of key-rings. In a small cage is a large sad bird – maybe a macaw. It looks flyblown and manky. I don't point it out to Anderson. He'd probably start a fight with the owner.

It's windy the next morning. Anderson says that's good, that it'll blow the cloud cover away. We walk down to reception to hire a car. We're going exploring. I have only just passed my test, so though I let Anderson put my name down too I do not intend to drive. They drive on the right, here. Anderson pulls out of the hotel car park and we almost hit a car, which is coming down the drive the wrong way.

'Cunts,' I say.

'Please,' says Anderson.

There is a newly sealed road we can drive along to a beach at the south of the island. Everyone says this beach is secluded. Everyone says, 'No one knows about it.' I am navigating, but I have to stop looking at the map every so often because Anderson is driving badly. He takes bends way too fast and can't get into third smoothly at all. I comment on this and he says, 'I know. It's difficult with my right hand.'

The inland scenery is strange and beautiful. There are mountains everywhere, bare and scored with lava trails. Cacti stand weird and spiky, looking like some humans would if they took off their body-masks. Planes fly overhead frequently, comforting, safe. We drive through a resort settlement. Golden couples amble hand in hand across the road in front of us; palm trees clatter in the wind. A sign says Turn Left For Reconstructed Native Village. It strikes me as strange, that Anderson and I are here trying to find some truth about ourselves, in this place that is fabricated, a fairy-tale, a lie.

The road to the secluded beach is unsealed. Red dust

rises from our little car. Anderson was right – the wind has
cleared the sky of clouds. When we arrive at the beach,
which is beautiful but crowded, it is the middle of the day and
the sun sits fat and high directly above us. The people on the
beach look slightly more like us than the people by the hotel
pool. There are no trees, just a deep stretch of white sand
leading down to the ruffled sea. I leave Anderson lying on a
towel with his book and go to stand knee-deep in the water,
feeling the hot wind against my shoulders, looking down
beyond the surface into the twisting yellow diamonds of sun
underneath. Anderson and I have been together for three
years. He has, to my knowledge, been faithful to me. I have
not returned the favour. I want children, for ignoble reasons
such as fear of loneliness and vanity. Anderson does not
want children. He is an advocate of depopulation. This is a
shame because Anderson, I think, would be a generous,
excellent father. He has nieces and nephews who adore him
and stand back warily from me. One of his sister's twin boys
used to scream 'Get out get out get out!' whenever I entered
a room he was in.

I walk further into the water until it is up to my waist. The
sun is burning heavily into my back in an almost obliterating
way. I wonder, if I turned round to look at Anderson, what I
would see. Maybe he's reaching over to pick up a ball and
throw it back to some smiling child. Maybe he's lost in his
book. Maybe he's explaining to someone how to get back
to the main road. Anderson has the sort of manner that
encourages people to stop and ask him directions. He looks
as though he is at home, wherever he happens to be. Over
by the rocks two boys are shouting, and splashing at each
other. Drops of water catch the sun, like crystals scattered in
the air. I bend my knees, push off with my feet and swim.

'You're not even here,' Anderson says.

There isn't any point in acting dumb. 'I'm sorry,' I say.
'Shall I make us some snacks?'

We are on our hotel-room balcony, tired and slightly burnt

after a day at the beach. Though I've had a shower, I can still smell salt in my hair. There's a bottle of wine open on the white plastic table and a bowl of pistachio nuts. I have bought some crackers, salami and cheese from the hotel store. I go to the sink bench and slice and arrange.

'You think food preparation is the answer to everything,' Anderson says from the balcony. It's a small room – he doesn't raise his voice.

'I'm sorry,' I say again. I take a plate of food out and put it on the table. I pour us some more wine. 'Maybe things just aren't working out.'

'Oh, shut up,' says Anderson. 'We're not going to have that conversation here.'

'Shall we write some postcards?' I ask.

We go through the usual jokes: wish you were her; weather's here, wish you were lovely, et cetera. I send a card to Jane, my parents and my anorexic brother. Anderson sends elegant descriptions of the native flora to his mother, to his sister, to his colleagues and to Nicholas, his friend who works for Amnesty International. On this card he writes: Thank God we defeated fascism so privileged dilettants like us can lie about in the sun without too much trouble from our consciences. He eats some salami, wipes his hands and smiles at me. I love Anderson's smile. It is not the smile of a good person, which goes to show that physiognomy counts for nothing. It is a dirty, wicked smile. I wish I saw it more.

'I love you,' I say.

'Don't sound so relieved,' he answers.

We get a bit drunk and each try to think of something personal to tell the other that they didn't already know. I remember how when I was at school we had a forty-hour fast and were allowed to eat nothing but barley sugars, and people sponsored us for each hour that we went hungry. The proceeds went to a charity organization helping famine relief in Ethiopia. I get to this stage of the story and Anderson begins a tirade against corrupt and unwieldy charities. 'But,' I said, 'what I did was get the sponsorship and then I was too starving to go without food so I ate anyway, then I kept the money.'

'That,' says Anderson, 'is not funny. It's not even charming.'

'Anderson,' I say, 'tell me again how we got together.'

'You know this story. We're supposed to be telling new ones.'

'Go on. Tell me anyway.'

'We met,' Anderson tells me as he strokes my ankle, 'at a dinner party given by your college friend Jane. There were four or five other people there, including the man with the blue shirt.'

'The man who looked like his head had been squashed in a vice,' I say.

'The man in the blue shirt,' Anderson says, 'who you were sitting next to.'

'Because Jane fancied you for herself,' I says.

'Because Jane and I had sponsorship projects to talk about,' says Anderson.

'Because Jane wanted to get into your pants.'

'Who's telling this story?'

I smile.

'The man in the blue shirt talked to you all night.'

'At me. He talked at me.'

'And I talked with Jane about the sponsorship plans but the whole time I was looking across the table at you. And you knew I was looking.'

'I did!' I say, and arch my foot.

'You knew, and you purposely didn't look at me. You pretended to be really interested in what the man in the blue shirt –'

' – with the squashed head –'

' – was saying to you. I thought, well, that beautiful girl really likes that guy. And everyone had coffee and you stayed, so I stayed but he stayed too –'

' – and Jane was hinting heavily that me and squash-head leave –'

'– and it was time to call for taxis and I said I was going north and you said you were going north too –'

'And Jane asked me if I'd moved and I told her I was minding my brother's place and she asked me if he'd moved and I said yes, north, he's moved north.'

Anderson holds my toes, tight. 'And squash-head was going west so we shared a taxi and you told me –'

'I told you –'

'You told me your brother hadn't moved but you just wanted the chance to have a conversation with me.'

'And that was that.'

'That was that,' Anderson says. 'And now we're here.'

We pack a picnic and set off for the crowded secluded beach again. Anderson's driving is really bad. 'Check your blind spot,' I remind him as he overtakes recklessly. 'And watch your following distance.'

'Angie. I'd never guess that you've just learned your road code.'

'Christ!' I exclaim as a car comes hooting towards us and changes sides at the last minute. 'No one around here can drive. Did you see that guy?'

'I'm identifying with him. Are you sure this is the right road?'

'Yes,' I lie, 'isn't this the way we came yesterday?'

'No. Are you looking at the map or what?'

'It's hard to tell just here,' I say. 'I think this is where we're supposed to be.'

'You think or you know?'

'I think I know.'

'Angie.'

'Don't pick on me.' My voice comes out more whiny than I mean it to.

'Fuck.' Anderson pulls over to the side of the road, braking harder than is strictly necessary. He snatches the map from my hands.

'What?' I say. 'Relax.'

'I have to do fucking everything,' he says loudly. 'You're completely thoughtless, you're so wrapped up in your own head. Jesus. You're doing my fucking head in.'

'Why are you with me then?' I shout this. 'Why? Because you like the way I look? I mean, that's really noble, isn't it, that's really admirable.'

'I'm sick of the fucking way you look,' he says. 'And don't fucking cry. There's nothing wrong with your life that a bit of selflessness wouldn't fix up.'

At this I get out of the car. I start walking down the road, and as I walk I begin to feel better. There is red gravel under my feet and the sky is empty. The mountains on my left loom closer and further away, like an optical illusion, depending on the cast of their shadows. I slip down the straps of my tank top so as to avoid tan marks. Anderson pulls up alongside, in the car.

The two boys I saw playing on the beach yesterday are here again today. I float on my back and watch them throw a red-white-and-blue striped ball back and forth to one another. They are brown-skinned, maybe Spanish. The older, skinny one has a protruding jaw and bat-like ears that stick out at an angle. His younger brother is beautiful. They throw the ball and laugh and call out. I think I can see which couple on the beach are their parents: a woman with curly blonde hair, cut short, and a dark-haired man with large eyes. He is rubbing suntan lotion into her shoulders. I kick a bit in the clear water and watch the birds gliding overhead. Then the ball lands next to me, splashing my face. I stand and lurch after it but its slick wet surface slips away from my touch. The older boy comes lunging towards me, a huge grin on his face, his hands flapping excitedly from the wrists, and I see that he has Down's syndrome. I push the ball towards him and it spins as it skims across the water into his arms, the coloured stripes rolling like a barber's pole.

'That boy's Down's syndrome,' I say when I flop back, dripping, on the towel next to Anderson. 'Or Mongol or whatever you say.'

'Down's syndrome,' says Anderson.

'His poor family,' I say, moving Anderson's snorkel from under my hip.

Anderson looks up from his book. 'Why?'

'Because. They must worry about him.'

'Not necessarily.' Anderson looks down again, and turns a page.

I would love to do some shopping while we're here but there really is nothing to buy. The resort shops peddle nasty sarongs and imitations of expensive watches. Electronic gadgets – personal organizers, portable CD players – are on sale everywhere but they don't do anything for me. There are no attractive local crafts. We walk past an outdoor leisure centre with a mini-golf course and Anderson gives me a history lesson. One of the men playing mini-golf leers at me. He's wearing Bermuda shorts. I wonder if Jane would ever tell Anderson about the affair that I had. She still has a thing for him. 'Blah blah colonization,' says Anderson, and I act interested and try not to think about the last time Jared and I had sex, on the floor of a hotel room in Amsterdam. I start singing the Joni Mitchell song again. A plane roars overhead.

'We're here,' Anderson says, 'so we may as well make the most of what's going on.'

By 'what's going on' he means the family entertainment in the cavernous bar of our hotel. It starts after dinner, which is an all-you-can-eat buffet of so-called Chinese food. Anderson has decided that tonight we should eat in the hotel and attend the G-rated cabaret. I don't feel in a position to argue as he hands over some money in exchange for our food vouchers. My entire daily budget has gone on pre-dinner drinks. I have trouble eating my chow mein without getting it on my chin.

Near the side of the bar we find wicker bucket seats and settle in with another drink each. Kids are running all over the place, squealing and giggling in instant holiday friendships. By

the wall some teenagers in last summer's fashions are trying
to act cool. The cabaret is instantly forgettable and involves
several over-tanned holiday reps with bad haircuts
lip-synching to hits from the 1980s. The children love it,
though, and I notice one kid, the boy from the beach,
bouncing in his chair and clapping along with great
enthusiasm. His mother, next to him, drinks a coloured
cocktail with an umbrella in the glass. His father wears a
checked shirt and holds the younger son on his knee.
Because he's skinny, you almost wouldn't notice the boy is
different. But he must be thirteen, too old to be jigging
around and clapping in that happy way. I feel tears pricking
my eyes.

We're in our hotel room. I'm kind of drunk. 'Did you see
him,' I ask Anderson, 'that mongoloid boy?'

He lets the incorrect label pass. 'No. I didn't notice.'

'It was so sad. His parents looked so brave. And his little
brother's normal but they were playing together just like
nothing was wrong.'

'Nothing is wrong. The kid's got Down's syndrome, that's
all. Why are you so obsessed with it?'

I think of the boy's smiling face in the coloured lights from
the stage and feel a rush of emotion. 'Because he – because
he's got something missing, he's defenceless, he's too soft.
What's he going to do when his parents die?'

'Be fine. Fuck's sake, it's not a major disability. There are
degrees. You're being sentimental and patronizing.'

The fact that Anderson is probably right again makes me
angry. 'I can't do anything right for you, can I?'

'Don't start.'

'I hate you.' I am overcome with a sudden desire to ruin
our holiday. We've been here only three days but it feels like
for ever. And I do hate Anderson, for taking me away from
my life, with all its distractions.

'You're drunk. Shut up.'

'You're a balding pompous cunt. I hate you.'

'Fuck off, Angie. I'm not going to take you seriously when you're like this.'

'You never take me sleriously. Seriously.'

'You're drunk.'

'You're a prick. I hate you.' Then I imagine the boy again and how Anderson would be if he had a son like that, how selfless and kind and persuasively normal. Anderson believes in people's essential goodness. It doesn't occur to him not to because he is that way himself. 'I love you, Anderson,' I say. It now seems to me that he's spent all this time with me as a sort of test. I want to be better, to make him feel that he hasn't failed. I want to live in a universe like his where we're all decent and equal, or could be if only we tried harder.

'I love you. I love you.'

'Oh, Angie,' he says, and his face, his beautiful sun-tanned cat-like face, looks as if something has cleared from it. 'You do right now. But you're still drunk.'

I start to cry. 'What's going to happen to us?' I say. 'I'm frightened of being alone.' I don't say, and I'm frightened of you as well.

Anderson ignores my tears. He sounds tired. 'Don't be frightened, angel. I'm here,' he says.

Entry:
- **If the door is open – knock and enter** (secretariat only)
- If the door is **closed** – knock and wait
- If the red light is on – don't **knock.**

Music:
- **Music** to be **played** at all times during **the day.**
- Take the **CDs** from the shelves **in strict** rotation.
- **Ensure that there** is sufficient music to be played while

out of the office (i.e. lunch time, **meetings.)**
- Put on new **CDs before** leaving at night.

William Sutcliffe
The Institute

**William Sutcliffe was born in 1971 in
London.** He has written two novels,
New Boy and the bestselling Are You
Experienced?, which has been
translated into nine languages. Both
books are published by Penguin, and
his third novel The Love Hexagon will
be published by Hamish Hamilton in
early 2000.

This is the true story of my encounter with the *Instituto Travesiano* in Italy. I have changed the Institute's name and location because, despite having stayed there for only one day, I am frightened of them.

My experience has its origins in an advertisement from the media pages of the *Guardian*. 'AMERICAN FOUNDATION SEEKS RESEARCHER FOR ONE-HOUR FILM TO BE SHOT THIS SUMMER' it read, with a return address at a *palazzo* in northern Italy.

Compared to the usual offers ('Corporate clients in Slough require researcher with two years' experience of working under intense pressure to extremely tight deadlines on very low pay for an in-house video about sludge'), this sounded like a job from heaven. So, that day, my handful of application letters included one addressed to the *Instituto Travesiano*.

Around a week later a tatty recycled envelope arrived from Italy, containing a treatment for the film and an explanation of the work done by the Institute. The treatment was entitled *Two Faces: A Life Approximating Sanity*, and read as follows:

We like the idea of Normal Society. We like that it hides – some people say purifies – our deepest fears. The ravings of Hamlet, the passions of Emily Dickinson, the colours and shapes of Van Gogh, the gibberings of Kurosawa's fools – we want these things pushed into a safe, hidden corner.

When I tell my friends of this film, why do they recoil? Someone tells me of weight problems, someone else about a divorce. A Japanese immigrant begins to talk to me about homesickness. Round another corner, people assume I can only be thinking of an information video. Where does one get help? Do they mean help, or simply Lithium?

So I kept myself quiet. The beasts behind this door must come out at their own pace – for too long they have been consuming me, destroying who I am. People are scared. Pandora must open the box in her own time. She must throw away notions of 'diagnosis' or 'hypochondria'. These agonies are mine, and they are real.

Dante knew that there was no Paradiso without the Inferno. Milton's Paradise was a Paradise Lost. Janus. The artist has two faces.

The time to hide is over. This film is about me.

The box is opening and the ghoulish shapes are beginning to dance. My fear, my agony, my despair at the ignorance of other people, my joy, my surges of intensity, my melancholy, my mania, my approximations to that chimera, sanity.

Of course, I should have taken one look at this document, thrown it in the bin, and forgotten about the job. It doesn't require great genius to conclude that when a mad person invites you to go and help make a film about how mad he thinks he is, you decline politely and retreat to a safe distance.

However, when you have been unemployed for four months, this is not the way you think. I managed to rationalize his writing style to myself, thinking that maybe he didn't speak very good English. I recognized that the treatment was a touch insane and was appallingly written, but I stifled any critical thoughts about what I had been sent. The words *'palazzo'* and 'Italy' at the top of the letter were the only two that interested me. I wanted the job.

The author of the treatment and Chairman of the Institute had an unmistakably English name (I shall call him Paul Hurst), so the excuse about the language barrier was a self-serving fantasy stemming, I suspect, from a deep-seated psychological craving to work in a place where it didn't rain all the fucking time.

The list of other projects undertaken by the Institute looked interesting: 'Latin American Artists Against Aids', a conference in Mexico City and the creation of a garden open

to the public – all operating from a *palazzo* near the Alps. I
simply didn't care what the film was about, or who would be
working on it – I just wanted to go there – to be in the sun,
near the mountains, living in a beautiful place with creative
people from all over the world, earning money, gaining
experience.

The letter specified that candidates should respond by fax,
giving their views on the project in not more than two
paragraphs. I decided that the best tactic was to send a reply
as pretentious as the treatment that they had sent me:

Dear Paul Hurst,
Thank you very much for sending me your treatment. It
sounds like a fascinating project, and one that I would be
very interested in getting involved with. The very fact that
people try and push mental illness away as a subject is
what makes it such an important topic to tackle. As you
point out in your treatment, it is deeply entrenched in
Western culture, but only in a glossed-over, sanitized form.
I think the idea of juxtaposing dramatic and literary
representations of depression with modern scientific
approaches is a clever and exciting way of placing an
important contemporary illness into a historical context,
and also of blowing the dust off these works of art.

Oliver Sacks' books sell well because they reassure us
that madness is something neurological, obscure and far
away from our everyday experience. The truth, that
depression and mental illness are mundane, widespread
and very painful, is one which people do not want to face.
The implication in your treatment is that your film will deal
as much with the embarrassment and hypocrisy
surrounding the subject, as with what it actually feels like
to go through a depression.

Yours sincerely,
William Sutcliffe

Not a bad letter, I thought. Vacuous, overblown, and dotted with hints that I thought his treatment was a masterpiece.

A few weeks later I was invited for an interview at a hotel in Belgravia. In order to keep up my I'm-as-pretentious-as-you-are persona, I dug out a black polo-neck to wear and prepared myself for concerted brow-wrinkling and chin-scratching.

I was invited into the room by the author of the treatment, Paul Hurst. He was wearing an expensive suit and designer glasses and had a thick crown of shiny brown hair, sculpted into the kind of style that can't survive more than a few hours without attention from a blow-drier. Although physically he wasn't a large person, he seemed to dominate the room, with a pair of huge, protruding green eyes. His small, wiry assistant with slicked-back blond hair, Maurizio Micheletti, almost vanished by comparison.

One look at their faces was enough to make it clear that this was a sense-of-humour no-go zone.

I had hoped that seeing Paul Hurst in person would solve the mystery of how someone with an apparently English name could write the language so badly. This mystery, however, only deepened: he spoke with complete fluency – as well as any English person – but with a hint of a foreign accent that wasn't Italian, but that I couldn't place anywhere else either.

I can't remember much of the interview. All I really recall is that I behaved like an arsehole, and that it went down a dream. When they asked me, 'Which part of film-making do you enjoy least?' I replied with something like, 'It's difficult to say. The process is so complicated that I find it impossible to separate out the different elements. One minute you might be making coffee for a sound-man, the next you might be helping with the script. To say you enjoy one aspect more than the other is wrong because it all has to be done – you simply can't separate them. I'm an ambitious person, but I understand that if you want to make films, you have to be familiar with every stage of the process.'

In other words – to translate that exchange into plain English:

'Will you do the shit jobs?'

'Yes.'

The rest of the interview continued in this vein, with badly disguised questions about how hard they would be able to make me work, to which I responded with the requisite cocktail of pushy ambition underpinned by a willingness to be ruthlessly exploited.

The crowning touch was when they asked me how well I spoke Italian, and I slipped instantly into the language, telling them I had worked in different parts of the country and that I spoke almost fluently. The more pretentiously I behaved, the more they seemed to like me. I was having such fun mimicking them, it didn't occur to me to worry that if everything went to plan, I would end up working for them and would have to carry on behaving in the same way.

It was one of those rare interviews where you walk out knowing that they loved you and that you have almost certainly got the job.

However, it was two months before I heard from them. The letter I eventually received had been written on a word processor but was printed out using a bizarre font in which it was impossible to tell a comma from a full stop.

Dear William Sutcliffe:

I am sorry for the time taken for this response. this is because once I produced the monster. it grows up on its own time-table: which is to be expected. and yet is more complex than I thought: a maize of difficulties. with branching paths. that is not quite finding the essence of the thing. & can only be more so as the weeks pass.

Celluloid. above all. defies the predictable. As such. I wanted to fix the key elements [director/screenwriter. etc.] before advancing.

We enjoyed meeting you very much & would like to offer you employment. starting in April & finishing end of Sept.

acting as assistant to Maurizio Micheletti & myself.

The work. for which you will be principally based in the office. at first may require of you some other duties. decreasingly so. naturally as the production nears filming. [We now expect an early Sept shoot.]

We will pay 400000 lire p wk: & board & lodging for the first month. Flights & transport to & from the Institute included.

As I anticipate. this is a job you will find very challenging. very satisfying & providing invaluable experience.

Please inform me. this week. by fax. as to your acceptance of the post.

Sincerely

Paul Hurst

I didn't have another job lined up for the summer, so it didn't even occur to me to think of turning this one down. I wanted to live in a *palazzo* in the sun, and I didn't see any reason to think about it further.

The next day I faxed back, accepting the job. This proved to be surprisingly difficult, since the fax number on the headed paper was obscured by a quotation printed in a miniature computer version of joined-up writing. While I couldn't read the number, the quotation was perfectly legible:

The city is of night, but not of Sleep; These sweet sleep is not for the weary brain.

The pitiless hours like years & ages creep, A night seems termless hell – James Thomson

While this was certainly useful information, I couldn't help feeling that it might have been marginally more practical to let me know the number they wanted me to reply on. Fortunately, I had kept a copy of the original advertisement, so I faxed it there.

Since I was by now back in temporary employment, at a TV production company, I gave them a number where they could fax me, and a few days later, I received a response.

> Dear William Sutcliffe:
> Thank you for your fax – sent wrongly to another fax no:
> 63 24. They have just passed it on to me.
>   When we met in London it was up in the air, for which
> no apologies are necessary.
>   It had to be like that. Now the time has come for
> practicalities.
>   Board & lodging for the period will be here at the
> Institute, which is, as you should know, in a unique setting.
> However it is isolated from the nearest village, going for a
> coffee or a drink [or whatever] needs some organizing – for
> – 6Kms away. From the observations of you I have already
> made, I can't think this is a problem: yet it is a factor that
> you must bear in mind with considerable care. Those
> uncomfortable with solitude, often find themselves uneasy
> here.
>   15th May: So when exactly could you leave? I think this
> is a reasonable date for commencement of your work –
> but if we wanted you to do any work in London – could
> you, how, when?
>   I will be grateful if you could fax me regarding the above
> & also give us a time when Maurizio could phone you – &
> where.
>   Sincerely
>   Paul Hurst

At the top of the fax, in the same tiny joined-up typeface as before, was another quotation:

I could see her predicament, I could touch it, it was like an opening
in her chest, a wound which she begged me to witness. She wanted
me to draw back the gates of her ribs & go inside to her deepest &
awfulest entity. I couldn't. It was too much, too chilling, too gapingly
wretched, for any, save herself. I drew back but she did not flare up

as was her wont. Perhaps it is this that makes us stalwarts in the end, this marriage of self with totally stranded self. Alone as a husk.
– Edna O'Brien

Nice to have a few heart-warming thoughts from Edna O'Brien as you prepare yourself for a new job, I thought.

I faxed him back, saying that I was looking forward to going. They then faxed me a contract for four months' employment, which I signed and returned.

The next letter I received was a week or so later (it is difficult to say exactly, because nothing I received from them ever had a date – only a thought for the day). The envelope, I noticed, gave off a strong aroma. It smelt like perfume. A spillage, I thought. They must have spilt something on the letter. Inside was a card signed by one of the secretaries, saying that it would be useful for me to know the rules of the Institute before I came. The rules applied only to visitors, rather than guests, she informed me – which was useful.

These rules ran to over ten pages, mentioned that the Institute was vegetarian, referred to the music that was played in the entrance hall, dealt with the use of the swimming pool and talked about scooters and bicycles for hire at the *palazzo*. It also explained how to use the laundry, which was available for residents. Overall, it gave me visions of a large artistic community, situated in the wilds of Italy, with groups of fascinating people from all over the world, including Latin American artists, working and living together in a fun (if faintly cranky) communal regime.

One thing which should have alarmed me was item four:

4. TELEPHONE
It is not permitted to make any phone calls on Institute phones. Only the payphone may be used. Staff members are forbidden to take any messages for anyone.

This, I assumed, applied to the visiting artists from around the world, rather than to myself, who would presumably be a

staff member, with my own phone. This assumption, it later
turned out, was wrong.

There were still several weeks before my departure, but
having read the rules I was now looking forward to going. The
summer pollution in London was building up, I was getting
bored with my job, and the thought of an Artistic and Cultural
Institute near the Alps seemed like a heaven-sent escape
route.

I had agreed to do odd bits of research for the Institute
before I left, and over the next few weeks I received
innumerable cards from Paul Hurst, asking me to find out
various things for him. All of them, I noticed, gave off the
same odour as the rules. Evidently, once you had accepted
employment from them, the reward was that they sent you
perfumed mail. Some of these letters were handwritten
scrawls which explained specific, and important events, for
example:

William Sutcliffe
We had a misfortune (SOMEWHAT) with the screenwriter. It
has been decided that I should take over the writing
myself – though, INDEED, I have never undertaken writing
for the screen before. Like most endeavours I suspect a
little application can blow away the mystique –
Though: nearer completion I shall require input from
someone (w. good film-writing record) for technical
aspects. PRACTICALITIES/IMPRACTICALITIES.
How we set about this I'm not sure – there are unlikely
to be 'lists' of such people – BUT: WHO KNOWS?
As with other communications bring and info with you.
Best wishes
PH

In his huge, randomly capitalized handwriting, this letter ran
to two pages, the first of which was on paper from the Hotel
Cipriani in Venice, the second on paper from the
Montalambert in Paris, both letterheads bearing five stars.

Other letters were carefully typed out on headed notepaper from the Institute but appeared to be about nothing at all:

Dear William Sutcliffe:
I am hoping to hear from you soon.
     One of the fascinating things will be, for us, & for you, I suspect, the international aspect of the process – therefore working with the English & the Italians. It is probable [I am hesitant to say anything too specific at this stage] that the crew will be mostly English, but one will have Italy, Italian bureaucracy, Italian builders, etc.
     This is something I want you to be very conscious of: [at least] two mentalities, approaches, customs, etc.
     I want you also to be aware that some individuals – because as you know we are talking about the film culture with powerful egos – that will try & exploit Mr Micheletti+s inexperience of working with an English crew: or perhaps there is an arrogance that things can only be done one way, the English way. & naturally we have to be absolutely clear that, whilst above all our loyalties lie with the project, yet internally, your loyalties should be with Mr Micheletti and myself.
     I hope it wont be as difficult as this: but nevertheless it is important to know these things at the beginning.
     Mr Micheletti will soon be taking over the very practical side of the production process.
     Best wishes,
     P H

This letter was cheerily capped with a quotation from Camus about resigning oneself to the misery and pain of the plague.
     By this stage, I did have considerable worries about the job and was convinced that I would possibly be working on the worst film ever made. However, this simply aroused my curiosity even more. The whole thing just sounded funny –

surreal, almost. If I was going to get paid, whether the film was good or not didn't seem to make too much difference. Whatever happened, I would be getting useful, hands-on experience of film-making, which was bound to be interesting and would look good on my CV. Since it was abroad, and the film was certain to sink without trace, I didn't see how it could do me any harm.

Also, in the back of my mind I was turning over my usual dream. I knew I didn't really want to work in TV and film. I wanted to be a writer. I was reluctant to admit it, but the more disastrous it sounded, the more I wanted to go. I needed some experience that would set me apart from the other day-dreaming graduates lounging around in London, half-heartedly working at jobs that half interested them. This, I thought, was certainly going to be unique.

A week or so before I was due to leave, I received my most aromatic document yet: eight pages on 'the policies' of the Institute.

This time, some of the information was really very, VERY, weird:

THE OFFICES:
– Keep the minimum of possessions in your desk.

YOUR AGENDAS:
– Paper: all entries must be in pencil.
– Note all meetings and things to be done.
– Make a note for Thursday morning to deal with and tidy all
  papers and computer files.

STYLE:
– Quote of the week at the top of all correspondence.
– Use the right font for the signature:
  PH – Colonna MT 12
  MM – Arial Narrow 12
  Secretaries: Monotype Corsiva 12

SIGNATURES:
PH – write P Hurst
PIH – write P (Imimketin) Hurst
Im – write Imimketin
Nothing – don't write anything
M – write Maurizio on the right
Others – own choice.

FOR MM AND JP'S OFFICES:
– Access to PH's office via MM's, except when doing the tour or
  requested to come up.
– Access to PH's via the blue stairway only by arrangement.

ENTRY:
If the door is open – knock and enter (secretariat only)
If the door is closed – knock and wait
If the red light is on – don't knock

MUSIC:
– Music is to be played throughout the day.
– Use the CDs from the shelf in strict rotation.
– Ensure that there is sufficient music remaining if you leave the
  office (e.g. lunch time, meetings.)
– Put on new CDs before leaving at the end of the day.

There were pages and pages of this kind of incomprehensible, insane advice. However, it still didn't occur to me to
think of backing out. The rules seemed so mad that I thought
they must be a joke. It was as if they were employing
five-year-olds rather than adults. Of course I knew they
couldn't be a joke, but I had decided to go, and I didn't want
to let myself get worried about it, so I read the "policies"
once and chose to forget about them.

Shortly before I left, I received one final letter from Paul
Hurst. It started with a request to find the telephone numbers
of the public relations offices of British Airways and Alitalia,
which seemed a little strange since I would have thought that

one of his three secretaries might have been familiar with the concept of a telephone book. However, by the second page it became clear that this was merely a preamble before he hit the real subject of his letter:

> Policy: WHEN in Italy . . .
> The European style of working/doing business is importantly more formal/distant than the US-BRITISH ways. (especially SHOWBIZ.)
>   Some people from UK/USA have – despite instructions from me – insisted on ignoring these warnings – CONSEQUENTLY it resulting in their losing respect/not being taken seriously.
>   I prefer the European way to the overfamiliar + OVER-INTIMATE BRITISH → (US)-way: it is clearer, and also less hypocritical, the practice of this requires a degree of accustomization – and no doubt you will learn, IF you want to.
>   At the Institute, we are →
> *MR HURST
> *MAURIZIO
>   More soon,
>   PH

I must have sent him a letter calling him Paul rather than Mr Hurst. Evidently this wasn't allowed, and that was what he was writing to tell me, in a spectacularly roundabout fashion.

A few days later I bumped into a friend who told me that she had applied for exactly the same job as me at the Institute but had recently been told that the film was postponed until next year. This was worrying, but something stopped me phoning to find out if it was true. I didn't want to hear any bad news. I wanted to work in Italy, in a *palazzo*, in the sunshine . . .

Not long after this, my aeroplane ticket arrived, along with details of how I would get to the Institute. I was due to fly to Milan on Sunday 14th May, from where I would get the train to Turin. I was booked into a hotel in Turin for Sunday night. On Monday morning, at '8H20', someone would pick me up and drive me to the Institute in time to start work that day.

On time, a chirpily subservient gardener driving a minibus collected me from the hotel. Just outside the town, we stopped at a car park and picked up two more passengers also on their way to the Institute: a second gardener and a secretary called Enza.

It emerged during the journey that they got this Institute bus to work every day. I asked why they didn't live in the *palazzo*, and they said that nobody did.

'What?' I said. 'Nobody lives at the *palazzo*?'

'Nobody,' said Enza.

'What about me?'

'Nobody except you,' she said.

'What about the Latin American artists?'

'Oh, that finished a long time ago,' she said.

'So how many people actually work there?'

'There's the two bosses,' she said, 'then three secretaries, a cleaning lady and two gardeners.'

'And you all just get a bus there in the morning, then leave in the evening.'

'Of course,' she said. 'Except that the bosses drive there themselves. They each have a BMW.'

I suddenly understood that he didn't mean an isolated community – he meant that I personally would be isolated, on my own, from the rest of society.

I began to feel worried.

After half an hour's drive the minibus parked at the end of a lane. I followed the other passengers through a large iron gate and into a beautiful garden full of wrought-iron sculptures. On my left, a spectacular vista opened up. I could see a wide, green valley dotted with villages rising gently into wooded hills. Looming above everything, in the distance, was the snowy summit of Monte Rosa.

On my right was the *palazzo*, rather smaller than I had expected, but impressive none the less – a two-storey building, at least thirty metres long, with curious baroque stylings in white and pink marble. There were a couple of ornate balconies, and a shady patio near the front entrance. A large clock with no face – just two twisted fingers of expensively sculpted iron – hung above the entrance to the building, looking strangely at odds with the otherwise kitsch façade.

Inside, I immediately sensed a strange atmosphere. Something cold and unhappy was hanging in the air.

Enza introduced me to Emma, the English girl who worked there, and told me that she would show me around. Emma was short and plump, with a flat curtain of greasy blonde hair hanging down on either side of her morose face. She had the look in her eyes of a zoo animal.

With an apologetic half-smile she led me down through the garden, past a swimming pool covered over with a leaf-strewn plastic sheet, to a small hut. I commented on the view, trying lamely to start a conversation.

'Best thing about this place,' she said.

She unlocked the door and led me into a tiny, windowless room with a bed, a sink and a chest of drawers. Incongruously for such bare living quarters, there was an expensive stereo system next to the bed.

Leading off the room was a small toilet, and a large shower, which contained a theatrical coat-hanger on wheels, presumably to compensate for the lack of a cupboard in the rest of the bedroom. The toilet and shower each had a window, but if the two doors had been closed, the room would have been dark.

Emma sat on the bed.

'How long have you been working here?' I asked.

'Two months,' she said.

'What's it like?'

She shrugged, and there was a long pause.

'Did you leave another job to come here?' she asked.

'No – I'd just finished a short-term contract.'

'At least that's something,' she said.

Cheery Emma really wasn't doing very much for my confidence.

'The two guys who work here,' I said, 'are they very weird?'

She looked me straight in the eyes for the first time. 'Yes,' she said. 'Very. But I hardly ever see them. They work upstairs.'

Back in the *palazzo*, I was introduced to the third secretary, Stefania, who showed me to my desk, telling me where to go in almost perfect English. She was one of those people who thinks it's funny to answer your questions with as little information as possible.

'Are you Italian?'

'No.'

'Are you English?'

'Sort of.'

'Do you have English parents?'

'Yes.'

'Were you born in England?'

'Yes.'

'Where?'

'London.'

'Whereabouts?'

'Hackney.'

'But you weren't brought up there.'

'No. Spain.'

This was all spoken with a would-be mysterious, I'm-so-witty smirk that made me want to kick her in the shins.

She showed me to my desk, which had nothing on it but an Apple Mac, and explained to me how things operated. No one has their own telephone, she said, and if you want to know something from a colleague, you're not meant to go and talk to them – you have to send them a message on the computer office-mail system. This is particularly important for Mr Hurst and Mr Micheletti, she said. If you want to speak to them, it is forbidden to go and knock on their door: you have to send them a message by computer, and they will send you a reply. If they want to speak to you, they will summon you via your computer, and only then do you have the right to go and knock on their door.

She wasn't joking, either. I was too shocked to ask her any questions. I just listened.

She went on to show me how the office-mail message system worked. 'Look – there's three messages for you already, from Imimketin.'

'What's Imimketin?'

'It's Paul Hurst.'

'What do you mean?'

'Imimketin's Mr Hurst.'

'It's a name? Why does he call himself Imimketin?'

She looked at me as if I was stupid. 'On the office-mail he's Imimketin, if you speak to him he's Mr Hurst and on letters he's PH. Haven't you read the policies?'

'Well – yes, but I didn't really understand them.'

'That's a matter for Maurizio Micheletti. Here's the software for your computer; you can install it while you're waiting for Mr Micheletti to arrive.'

'OK.'

My three messages from Imimketin were a list of the rules, a brief welcome, and a message saying that he was very busy today and would see me at 18:15. I couldn't tell whether or not he was in the building.

I looked back over the rules, which I had brought with me, and spotted in my pile of documents the first letter they had sent me. I noticed that it contained an explanation of Mr Hurst's other name.

> Paul Hurst founded the Instituto Travesiano in 1994. The 1st project was to invite underprivileged Latin American Tribesmen to attend a 10 week course at the Institute's headquarters, The Palazzo of Travesiano. This madness was scorned by the so-called Peruvian intelligentsia, for whom the Jivaro are mere primitives.

The Jivaro honoured him with a name, normally given only to Kings and Warriors: Imimketin! [He who clears the path].

Imimketin continues to clear fresh paths. Recently he announced with pride: I am president, I am queer, I am manic-depressive. This offended many, amongst them the local newspapers, who refused to print an advertisement with such a heading.

And now he has the audacity to make a film on maybe one of the greatest taboos . . .

So – his office-mail name came from Jivaro tribesmen. I should have guessed, really.

I spent the morning installing disks on to my computer. I was sharing an office with Enza, who had been perfectly friendly to me on the bus, but now, in the office, she barely spoke to me.

Then a message popped up on my screen, saying that I should go and see Maurizio Micheletti. To get to his office, I had to go down the main staircase, through the secretaries' room downstairs (Emma coyly caught my eye but didn't smile or say hello), then up a small winding staircase at the back of the building.

I knocked on the thick metal door and was summoned into a large room. Although it was a warm day the windows were closed and the office was artificially heated to a stifling temperature. Maurizio, however, was wearing a jumper. He perfunctorily asked me how my journey had been, then started reading through a list of things for me to do.

He told me that all employees had to write a list of the tasks they had been given to do every morning and send it to him by computer. Then, every evening, the list had to be sent again, detailing exactly which tasks had been done and which were outstanding. Everything had to be done in the strict order of priority that had been given by Mr Micheletti, but if a message came through from Mr Hurst, then that immediately had top priority and had to be done straight away.

I had to interrupt him to begin my complaint.

'I'm sorry,' I said, 'but I'm a bit worried about my role here. I didn't realize I would be quite so isolated. I had the impression that other people would be living here as well.'

'Oh.'

'It seems that everyone leaves at six o'clock, then I'm all alone in the *palazzo*.'

'No – myself and Mr Hurst usually work until much later than that.'

'Yes, but . . .' My voice tailed away. I didn't know what I could say.

After a pause, he said, 'We'll see how it goes,' then he continued reading through his list of things for me to do.

I couldn't listen, partly because I was stifled by the heat, partly because my mind was racing with fears. I knew I would be utterly miserable if I stayed, and I was desperately trying to calculate how long I would be able to stick it out, whether they would pay me anything if I broke my contract before the four months were up, or whether I should just leave straight away.

Some of the things I was supposed to do were to 'find a company who can help us keep absolutely up to date with technology,' looking in Paris, London and Barcelona and 'look for a caravan – we want one for a new sculpture for the garden.'

As far as the film went, he said that Mr Hurst was working on the script, and that our job would be to deal with the 'concrete' (he said the word as if it were highly distasteful to him) aspects of the film, in order to leave Mr Hurst free for the 'imaginative and creative' side of the work.

The work on the film seemed so vague, with the script not even finished, that I remembered what my friend had told me just before I left.

'Is it true that the film has been postponed until next year?' I said.

'That's correct,' he replied. 'At the moment, we're considering a January shoot.'

I was flabbergasted. They'd hired me to work on a film that wasn't even happening.

'Are there any questions you want to ask me before you get started?'

I was so confused that all I said was, 'Yes – there are certain aspects of the rules that I don't quite understand.'

'Send me a message, detailing exactly what you don't understand, and I will appoint someone to explain it to you.'

'It's OK,' I said, 'Enza is in my office – I can ask her. They're only small questions.'

'No – she has her own work to do. You shouldn't interrupt her. Send me a message saying exactly what you want to know, and I will appoint someone to help you.'

I went back to my office via the kitchens. I needed a glass of water and asked the cleaning lady where the glasses were kept. She showed me, but told me I had to take a tumbler. 'The stemmed glasses are reserved for the management,' she said.

I installed the software, my head spinning. I had only been there half a day, but I now knew that I had to leave as soon as possible.

A message popped up on my screen, saying that my lunch-hour was from 12:30 to 1:30. Enza told me, at 12:33, that I should go. It's best to stick to the times exactly, she said.

'Are you coming?' I asked.

'No. Mine is 12:45 to 1:45.'

I wasn't alone in the kitchen, however, since a gardener and the cleaning lady were both in the middle of their slightly earlier lunch-slots. Rather than the communal cooking I had imagined, everyone had their own Tupperware pot of food which they heated up in a microwave oven. Although I had free board, it emerged that I had to cook for myself. Each week, the cleaning lady would ask me what I wanted from the supermarket and buy it for me. She wasn't allowed to buy meat, though, because Mr Hurst and Mr Micheletti were vegetarian. If I wanted meat, I would have to pay for it myself.

As a special treat, because it was my first day, the cleaning lady had made lunch for me. I thanked her and said that I would take it outside and eat it in the sun. Before I could take one step towards the door, she grabbed my arm and told me that this wasn't allowed – I had to eat in the dining room with the others.

I followed Stefania (who had the same lunch-hour as me) to a dark room at the back of the *palazzo* with bare concrete walls interrupted only by one tiny window just below the ceiling. This was the staff dining room. When I went back to the kitchen to get a drink, the cleaning lady rushed up to me and spoke in an exaggerated whisper. 'When that door is closed,' she said, 'it means that they are eating. You mustn't knock, and you absolutely mustn't go through. If you want to get back to your office, you have to go outside through this door, across the garden, and in through the door at the other side of the building. I'm serving them at the moment.' Then she rushed to pick up two bowls of soup, which she took into the adjacent room.

I spent the afternoon at my desk, wrestling with my sluggish computer, deleting the majority of the files that I had installed in an attempt to stop it running so slowly. Since the only way of getting help with the computer was sending computer messages to other people, it took the whole afternoon to figure out what the problem was. I would send a message to Maurizio telling him what was wrong, he would send one back telling me what to do, I would send him another one telling him that it hadn't worked. And so on. It was only after ten or so of these exchanges that Maurizio finally came to help me.

After that I wrote my list of the items in the rules that I didn't understand (how to send faxes, what to stamp the faxes with, where the papers and pens were kept, and so on). I sent this to Maurizio, then got a message from Stefania saying that I should go down and see her, and she would explain things to me.

When I got back to my desk, there was a message waiting from Maurizio, saying that I should go to his office at 16:15, and in the mean time I should familiarize myself with the film books in the library.

The library contained three or four reference books on film and a glossy 1993 film diary. I looked at the pictures in the diary, then sat down with a novel which I found on a different shelf, and waited until 16:15. In those two hours, I read no more than fifteen pages. I had to read each sentence several times, as my mind flew away from the words on the page to rehearse over and over again what I would say at the meeting.

By now I knew I had to leave. The place was like the headquarters of a religious cult without the religion. Part of me felt I should stay for a week just to see what happened, but I knew that if I did this, my chances of getting paid for the week, once I had broken the contract, were minimal.

One problem was that I had been requested to buy an enormous film-industry reference book for them in London, which had cost me seventy pounds, and I had to find a way of making sure they reimbursed me for it. In order to do this, I would have to resign with as little acrimony as possible. If I told them I was disturbed by all the rules, I had the feeling this might backfire against me. The secretaries, particularly Enza and Emma, were clearly genuinely afraid of Paul Hurst. Without even having clapped eyes on him, I too had been infected by this fear.

I decided that I would just stick to one clear story, with one complaint (the lack of a film), then there couldn't be any real argument. After all, they had sent me the rules in the post, and even though on paper they were incomprehensible, I thought they might have been able to use the fact that I had read them to suggest that I had known exactly what I was getting into, and that now I was changing my mind. If I could

just retreat as humbly as possible, there was a chance I
might get my seventy pounds back.

Were it not for this money, and for the fact I was unlikely to
be paid any salary, I would have stayed a little longer. I was
curious. I wanted to find out how Paul Hurst did it – how he
scared people so much that you were afraid of him before
you even entered his office.

At 16:15 I went to Maurizio's office and knocked at the
door. There was no answer. I would have poked my head
around the door, but I guessed that was probably against
regulations, so I went back down the stairs, through the
secretaries' rooms, up my own staircase, and sent him a
message saying that he wasn't there when I knocked.

Ten minutes later a message flashed up on my screen
saying that he was now ready to see me and that I should
bring the book I had brought from England with me.

I went back to his office, gave him the book and
ostentatiously presented him with the receipt. When I had
explained to him how to use the book, he sat back and
picked up his list of things for me to do.

Just after he had finished his first sentence, which I didn't
even hear, I told him that there was something I had to say.

'I'm sorry,' I said, 'but I think there's been a mis-
understanding. You hired me to work on a film, and now it
appears that it isn't even happening. This other work that
you're giving me isn't what I came for. It's not what I'm
interested in. So I don't think there's any point in me staying
here.'

There was a silence, while he looked out of the window,
stroking his chin. Then he spoke.

'Go back to your desk, and I will send you a message.'

I almost asked for my money, but the conversation had
ended so quickly that I hadn't quite got up the courage. I
walked out of the door, immediately furious with myself for
this cowardice.

A few minutes later a message flashed up on my screen
saying, 'Re: final interview. Come to PH's office IMMEDIATELY.'

His office was huge, full of expensive furniture, with four sticks of incense burning in a tall gothic stand in the middle of the room. It was the first time I had seen Paul Hurst since my interview with him several months ago.

As soon as I had entered, he started shouting at me.

'SO YOU'RE BREAKING YOUR CONTRACT, ARE YOU?'

His face was crimson, one cheek twitching slightly, and his bulging eyes were straining at the leash of their optic nerves. *OK*, I thought, *my curiosity has been satisfied. This is how he frightens people. The secret is, look like you have absolutely no control over yourself, then tremble as if on the verge of physical violence. If you can do this convincingly, you're in charge. You're scary. Fine. Now all I want is to get out of here with my seventy quid, and without facial contusions.*

'I really am sorry but . . .'

'I HAVEN'T GOT TIME FOR YOUR APOLOGIES.'

'Well, OK. What I mean is, you hired me to work on a film, and there doesn't seem to be a film happening, so there's nothing to keep me here.'

'You obviously have your head full of ludicrously romantic ideas about what the process of film-making involves. Did you honestly think you'd be working on the film straight away?'

'I was under the impression that . . .'

'DID YOU THINK THAT YOU'D BE WORKING ON THE FILM STRAIGHT AWAY?'

'I thought my job would include preparations for the shoot, then work on the shoot, then I'd be going home. I came here to get experience on a film. That's what I'm interested in.'

'We're not here to provide experience for whatever takes your fancy, you know. We advertised for a researcher.'

'Yes, but in the interview you said you wanted a production assistant. I came here to do a specific job, and now you seem to want me to do something completely different. I'm sorry, there's obviously been a communication problem.'

'I'M NOT INTERESTED IN WHETHER OR NOT YOU'RE SORRY. We've wasted a lot of money on flying you here and on your

hotel. I'm very angry. There's a bus to Turin at 6 p.m. You
should leave on that.'

'Could I not spend one night here? Then I've got time to
arrange some travel home.'

'No – absolutely not. Get out.'

I stroked my chin for a few seconds. (It was obviously
catching.)

'Could you reimburse me for the book, please?'

'We've wasted quite enough on you already, but I suppose
so. Go next door.'

Maurizio took me through into his room, wordlessly wrote
me out a cheque, then I left.

I went downstairs. In the main office, Stefania and Enza
were working on their computers. I told them what had just
happened and instantly all their coldness towards me
vanished. They both started chuckling and shaking their
heads. They told me they had seen it coming before I had
even arrived. Stefania instantly started helping me with ringing
British Airways and arranging a flight home, and Enza came
up close to me and whispered, 'Don't tell anyone, but I'll put
you up for the night and take you to the railway station in the
morning. Don't say anything now – I'll speak to you on the
bus.'

After I had booked a flight for the following day, I went and
spoke to Emma. For the first time, she had a smile on her
face. She, too, whispered to me.

'I overheard what you said. You're doing the right thing. I
wish I'd got out straight away, too.'

'Why don't you leave?'

'I left my job in England to come. I moved here with my
boyfriend, and he's working round here, too. I can't leave
until I get another job somewhere else. I'm stuck.'

'Oh, no.'

'I'll be out of here soon, though. I'm writing ten letters a day.
If you need somewhere to stay, I can put you up for the night.'

'It's OK, thanks. Enza's already offered, and she can take
me to the railway station in the morning.'

'All right. But if you're stuck . . .'

'Thanks.'

'I knew it would happen. I wanted to write to you and tell what it's like here, but I was afraid you might show the letter to Mr Hurst.'

Since leaving England I had hardly eaten anything. My nervousness, growing into outright fear, had taken away my appetite. The minute the bus drew away from the Institute, suddenly I was famished.

On the bus to Turin, I chatted to one of the gardeners.

'It's the Middle Ages in that place,' he said to me. 'I'm OK – I get well paid, I dig a few holes, mow the lawn – but they're crazy people. I hate going inside that building.'

Just outside the town we stopped at a car park. I got into Enza's car, and we drove for another twenty minutes to her house.

She told me that she had been there for seven months, but that she still didn't have a clue where any of the money to fund the Institute came from. They claimed to have an office in America, but none of the secretaries had ever heard from it.

Although we spent most of the evening talking about the Institute, I never really found out anything more. She said I had left before seeing how awful it got. She said that they bullied the staff, and that any complaints rebounded on you, causing them to treat you even worse. They gave vague, incomprehensible orders, and if you interpreted them wrongly, you were humiliated and insulted for being stupid. If you argued back, they punished you, for example, by forbidding you from riding in the Institute bus. Once, Emma was told that she was not allowed any lunch because she had made a mistake.

All Mr Hurst's orders were given in English, but if Enza didn't understand them, she wasn't allowed to ask Emma for help and had to ask Mr Hurst for clarification via the computer. One time, she was caught asking Emma to translate a word, and they were both shouted at.

Enza told me that she couldn't get the Institute off her mind at the weekends, and that she often dreamed about it at night. However, the region was depressed, and there were few other jobs available. If she left voluntarily, before finishing her contract, she would receive no unemployment pay. All staff were made to sign long contracts before they started, so the secretaries there were all trapped. Stefania was an exception because, Enza suspected, she received special treatment in return for informing on the other secretaries – telling Maurizio and Mr Hurst what was said about them behind their back. In return, for example, Stefania was allowed to use the phones.

Despite the enforced contracts, they had reputedly been through twenty-two secretaries in three years.

As for what the Institute actually accomplished, that remained a mystery. *Two Faces: A Life Approximating Sanity* hasn't yet appeared at my local cinema.

Grant Morrison

It was the 90s

**Grant Morrison is the writer of a
number of successful graphic
novels and comic book series**
including Batman: Arkham Asylum, The
New Adventures of Hitler, St Swithin's
Day, Doom Patrol, Kill Your Boyfriend
and Flex Mentallo, Man of Muscle
Mystery. Most recently he wrote the
monthly titles The Invisibles and JLA for
DC Comics. He is also the author of the
award-winning plays Red King Rising
and Depravity and numerous other
things besides. 'It was the 90s' is a

true story.

1.

Karachi, pre-dawn. The plane's been on the Tarmac for an hour, refuelling. Through the window, darkness resolves into airport buildings, flat roofs, dozing aircraft. Emergent sunlight is developing the city like a photograph in a tray; grainy forms sharpen to Polaroid precision. A city that looks like none I've ever seen before is slowly floodlit until every little stone and particle of dust casts a fierce black shadow.

'Karachi . . .'

It isn't the first time either of us has stated the fucking obvious and I fear it won't be the last.

Me and my old pal Ulric have decided we need to visit Kathmandu. He and Janice have a baby on the way; this may well be the last time that we get to do something this stupid. A few ambient albums into the decade and we've come all the way from Glasgow to claim the almost-instant enlightenment promised in a recent Sunday-night God-slot special, which followed a likeable man in a hat down from Kathmandu to the plains of India in the footsteps of the Buddha.

If Buddha could attain enlightenment at age thirty-five, then surely nothing can stop *us* attaining it right now. Are we not younger and sexier than Prince Siddhārtha?

In Kathmandu there is a *stupa* by the name of Swayambhunath, which demonstrates one of the difficulties inherent in writing about this part of the world; it all turns into Rudyard fucking Kipling given half the chance. The promise is given that any pilgrim who dares ascend the temple's three hundred and sixty-five stairs WITHOUT ONCE STOPPING TO REST is guaranteed enlightenment in this life.

Psychedelic post-mods, cynical and wonderstruck, simultaneously believing everything and nothing, we have only one concern in our minds.

What form will our enlightenment take?

I'm laughing sarcastically now as the plane goes up into the dawn and have no idea that I'll be returning home in a week with the conviction that the structure of space-time has been explained to me by my own unfolded fifth-dimensional self.

'We're on the wrong side to see the Himalayas.'

The captain's just relayed the bad news. There's a moment of horror that our off-the-peg Gonzobeatnik adventure's in danger of getting off to a flat start and then we settle back to view the most boring scenes available to anyone in a plane flying over the planet's most impressive mountain range. The sky momentarily tie-dyed applegreen, saffron, like paint atomized across a canvas.

The pilot's right.

2.

Later, we are flat out on little beds in the Kathmandu Guest House, deep in the heart of Thamel, the town's bubbling tourist sink. Football's popular here and the local teams are Kathmandu and Bhaktapur. The guy who sold us our divots of Afghani hash was once a keen player but his belly had 'become fat'. Cheap holidays in other people's mystery. Ulric and I spent our first day thus, trawling disconnected through the wrecked, evocative landscape of fat corpses and half-naked kids on bomb-site garbage tips, past the roundabout where the cars veer like dodgems. I'm utterly at home. When I dream about Glasgow, it looks like this; post-nuclear, beautiful.

'If those pigeons don't stop cooing I shall lose my wits, Shelley!'

I turn my head to watch the telephone burning on the table between our beds. I stare for a little while. Ulric's in the background, staring, too.

Suddenly we're moving rapidly, dousing the blaze with lemon soda. The candles we bought to give the room some atmosphere have surrealized the telephone. Molten plastic sizzles on the tabletop.

'It's like Salvador Dali.'

We get up and head out into launderette temperatures.

3.

What seem like straight roads on the map turn into tangled chaos when we hit the Territory. It's like fractals; a neat line in the guidebook can never hope to hint at the knotted, fuming alley-ways and infernal thoroughfares which form its real-life counterpart. It's impossible to take a deep breath. It's impossible to take even a shallow sip of air without toxins settling nicely at the back of the lungs. Both of us are aware of a thin, persistent whine in the head, like a broken light bulb vibrating on a steel table. The petrochemical buzz, the old fossil-fuel kick, low and mean, like glue. We struggle through the traffic and the crowds, the perpendicular surging tides of Nepalis, searching for someplace to slow down and gasp a lungful of oxygen. We seem to be time-travelling, the city's regressing around us, back to its origins.

'Must be the old part of town . . .'

The *sindur*-splattered shrines here in these sudden dusty squares are prayed down to abstraction. Vague elephant heads, Garuda and Indra desculpted back to smooth stone by generations of votive fingers; inarticulate altars to the first shapeless, archaic powers. Scabby dogs curl into commas to nibble and scissor at sores in their haunches. There are buffalo feet, hacked to the open bone, bleeding against walls. Skinny children with sticks, running, yelling. Bicycle bells ring as tall geriatric buildings loom up around us, with windows like gunshot wounds in clay. Ancestral houses, ghosts from somewhere back down the evolutionary line of the building trade. Ancient graveyard souls our tower blocks recall only dimly.

'We've been here before.'

This isn't about reincarnation, we're lost now in a Hampton Court maze of open-sewer smells, rich spices and yellowed, ancient light. Buildings like bad teeth tower overhead, delirious in their decay. Hunched together like widows, reducing the overhead sky to a white knife-edge. Everything feels like a memory.

'We're fucked.'

And for a timeless moment it seems as though we are; doomed to spiral meaninglessly through these endlessly interconnected streets and squares like glitter in a paperweight. Then mythic time bursts like a boil and we're ejected into Durbar Square, the medieval hub of Kathmandu and our intended destination of several hours past.

It's like 'Soylent Green'; the population explosion has left every square inch of the planet's surface covered in jostling biomass and we're right in the middle of it. Snatched up by swirling weatherfronts of touts and tourists, it's impossible to stop or look at anything. I hold my camera up over my head and snap blindly, hoping for the best, trapped on a Disney ride, with no control over our brief journey through an animatronic landscape. We have no way of interacting, we can only watch as the square is spun around like a special effect and we're looped and threaded through the press of bodies, vaguely aware of an impressive congregation of huge black timbers and sloping roofs. Buddhist demons contort their faces at us from the façades of temples and palaces, legions of carved skeletons are dancing or fucking; it's a swingers' paradise in the underworld.

'This definitely looks like the most interesting part of Kathmandu . . .'

'Fuck it.'

We're thrown off the wheel, out along the spokes of stress Zombies shouldering through shoals of touts waving daggers and incense we don't want, drugs we don't need. Somebody's shoving yet another crudely fashioned musical instrument in my face, yet another carpet. My brain feels like it's leaking out my nose as a thin gruel of wasted neurons. I cast an agonized glance at Ulric. We're metamorphosing into Buddhist demons ourselves, as these weak Occidental physiologies fail to adapt to the seething carbon-monoxide atmosphere of Kathmandu.

'Have you noticed how our noses run constantly?'

'We're breathing industrial pollutants as though they were air, what do you expect?'

We can both feel delicate nasal tissues turning to lace and pulp.

'A month in this place, you could breath on fucking Jupiter.'

It's sheer endurance now. Nothing else is keeping us walking. We can only wonder if we'll make it home through the labyrinth before our lungs give out and our heads crack open like bad eggs.

'There's no way back to Thamel. We'll be found dead here and they'll stick our skeletons up there to be shagged daft by the rest of those randy cadaverous bastards.'

'No. I've got an idea. Squint your eyes a bit and scan for white faces.'

The trick's remarkable, better than a compass. Little by little, the pale faces bob together like balloons, clustering, streaming. We take every turning that leads on to any road where the milling, sallow moons seem to outnumber their native counterparts. Soon there are hardly any dark blobs at all hovering at head height.

We refocus and we're on Thamel Chowk.

It could be Camden on a Saturday.

4.

The pigeons never stop cooing and burbling. Our room floats at the bottom of a white well. Drowned in an undersea prison.

'It's like one of those fucking Denholm Elliot things.'

'Colonial heat. Him in a Panama hat.'

'Whitewashed walls, sweat stains on shirts . . .'
The hash is making us telepathic.

Night soaks in. Thunder on the peaks. A skin of peeling
dove-grey vapour curdling off the mountaintops.
Swayambhunath is floodlit, glowing white and spectral
against the flaring sheetmetal glare of lightning. The painted
eyes of Buddha.

5.

Dinner in the courtyard outside the KGH. The waiters come
and go like automatons on an Eastern European clocktower
but we get talking to one guy. He sizes us up and says we
should meet somebody called 'JAH!'
  Not quite the laid-back 'Jaaaaah' sound of Rastafarianism,
this name is pronounced as the crack a .50-calibre
armour-piercing shell makes when it leaves the barrel of a
semi-automatic sniper rifle and travels towards your brain at
2,600 feet per second.
  'Jah! Ask for Jah!'
  Ulric and I are baffled but we smile and try to retain some
control over the situation. There's something about the
combination of the man's strange, knowing leer and the
paranoia-inducing chemicals we've been necking merrily all
day; we're primed to find and extract the essence of the
utterly inexplicable in even the most ordinary encounters.
There are too many unrecognizable emotional nuances in
everything the waiter is saying.
  'Jah!'
  We nod, sweating.
  'Jah! Yes, we will,' we say desperately. 'If we need
anything at all. Ask Jah!'
  Our attempts to duplicate the name fail to capture its
ballistic qualities but appear to satisfy the waiter. With a final
conspiratorial smirk, he leaves to bring us our order. We look
at one another.

We never come up with a good enough reason to ask for Jah. He's still there for all I know.

6.

Just around the corner from the KGH, on Chhetrapati Thamel, the Blue Note bar does jazz and blues for wannabe beatniks. The vodka's like water so rum and Coke looks like the best bet. Up on the roof garden, glasses are chimed.
   'The systematic derangement of the senses!'
   'Let's be drunk for ever!'
   No dice: the Blue Note sheds its customers at half-past ten, whereupon Ulric and I hit the streets and embark on an Impromptu *derive*, losing ourselves in a sodium-lit shadow-city of rotting garbage heaps, cratered waste lots and fallen walls. All colours are the same colour. The roads are deserted. Kathmandu smells of damp plaster in the cellar, of piss and cinnamon. Crumbling paintjobs are held together by torn posters for local events and Indian films. The whole city's smouldering like incense in the night's radiant heat, haunted by Hindu gods and bodiless Tibetan masks, Kathmandu dissolving in the dark.
   We chance upon a procession, glimpsed in the vertical Cinemascope between houses. Weird, shining rites in German Expressionist alleys. The sleighbell sounds and devotional chants mesmerize us, like children drawn to the glamour of an adult party. Candlelight throws flaring shadows and scintillates off sequinned saris. We zoom in. The light and chanting get closer, and something like a merry-go-round is sailing towards us down the lanes. A circle of shimmering dancers closes in.

Up on the roof garden of the Kathmandu Guest House, I'm lying on the ground, tittering and twitching. Clouds and sky wheel overhead.
   'One chocolate rupee.'
   It seems like the funniest fucking thing we've ever heard in

our lives. Except for 'Ganesh Triangle' which comes close.

A bald German makes a stand for common sense, his face rising like the moon over Berchtesgarden as he ascends the ladder to the roof.

'It's nearly dawn . . .' he snarls.

'No it isn't.'

The man has no defence against the plain truth and descends, cursing.

Back in the room, I find splashes of blood on my trousers. I'm sure they must have come from my vandalized nose but other possibilities loom horrifically.

'Christ, we've sacrificed a goat. It's ''Blood for Kali'' on a Tuesday, isn't it?'

'Tuesdays and Saturdays . . .'

Lying in bed, listening to 'Kill Rave', head aflame. I'm seized with uncontrollable panic; burning phones, dodgy rum, drugs, annoying our friends from the EEC, exploiting Third World economies, mysterious bloodstains . . .

'We're not beatniks, we're not romantic poets we're *Euro-louts*.'

We need some enlightenment and we need it fast.

7.

In the morning, I take a few pictures of the charming, cross-eyed tomcat on the roof before we set off for Swayambhunath and the assault on transcendence.

It's a short walk past roadside shrines and concrete flatblocks encrusted with satellite dishes. Standing at the foot of the hill, three hundred and sixty-five steps from the summit, we swig some water and take deep breaths, oblivious to the swarming salesmen. We start off strongly and by step fifty or so (somewhere in February of this Year of Stairs), we realize we've overtrained for the event. We take to the climb like bats to darkness. One bound, no pauses for breath, guaranteed enlightenment in this life. *That's how easy it is.*

Swayambhunath ('the self-created') is two thousand years old and is considered by Tantric Buddhists to be the principal focus of power in the entire Kathmandu Valley. Any devotion performed here, it is said, will be thirteen billion times more meritorious than devotions performed elsewhere.

'Christ! I hope it's enough . . .'

The *stupa* meditates, eyes wide open, in a haze of piss and steaming rubbish. Savoury wafts of charcoal and soot and painted candlesmoke. Endless Buddhas, trinket shops, families of monkeys squabbling in the trash and the splash of saffron paint on everything, like dawn light. Lines of prayer flags tether the *stupa* dome to the hilltop. Faceless cosmic eyes drawn below the golden spire above the dome, the uninflected gaze of Buddha. The sacred and the profane indistinguishable.

Under the trees on the path around the back of Swayambhunath, we share a bar of Maya Gold chocolate Ulric brought from home. I will for ever associate its flavour with the colour of saffron paint. An Indian file of monks passes wielding hand-held prayer wheels like football rattles. One of them turns to look at me and smiles like Yoda. I can't help smiling back.

We take photos. Drums play.

Time to get out of Thamel.

8.

Our new room's at the Vajra or 'Bazhra'. On the way there, I buy a little statue of Ganesh. The god is seated at what looks like a Vedic word processor. Weird machines of the Rama empire, translating thoughts into Sanskrit texts. It'll look good on the desk back home.

We track along the left bank of the Bishnumati river. The water surface bleached white, etched with infected paisley patterns, fern-shapes of drain water and oil. Kids are paddling in a coffee-coloured froth that laps at the tumbled rubbish heaps. Mountains of seething refuse smoke and buzz, melting in the day's white heat. Lidded skies and hazes of dust and ozone. Lightning storms warm of the approaching monsoon. Pigs, unconcerned, sort through the shit with meticulous snouts. Huge black boars slide into the water, neck deep in crap, blood temperatures falling.

The Vajra's a strange oasis of green oxygen above the barking, ringing chaos of town but our week is taking its toll. Ulric's sick, belching sour gas. I feel fine but I'm farting water and have to be very careful.

While Ulric's 'lying down', I sit for a while on the roof garden, looking towards Swayambhunath. The *stupa* looks back. Today's the big match and I can see Kathmandu and Bhaktapur battling it out on a dirt field nearby. It's our last day and I'm restless. Something is approaching from the perimeters as I turn my attention to the temple on the hill. A goal is scored, the cheering rises and rises and Swayambhunath begins to change shape.

I've had hallucinations before. I'm familiar with the full range of effects of all the major psychedelic drugs. I've had fevers and rigours and shared sustained, intimate contact with many of the most grotesquely disordered mental states available to humanity. I've eaten a few lentil-sized hash pellets, that's all. I tell myself all this but as I hurry back downstairs, I realize I'm in the middle of something quite new. Ulric's out for the count. I make it to my bed and stare up at the room's latest arrivals.

There are one or two entities *interacting* with the space I'm in. They look a little like the morphing, liquid-chrome blobs from rave videos; capable of emerging from and returning to the substance of the furniture and even the air itself. Although I'm definitely in the room – calm and pleasantly spartan, with its wooden beds and shutters, its firm and sensible bolsters – I'm simultaneously aware of something bigger than the room, something of which the Vajra, Nepal, and the entire universe beyond are simply cross-sections. I'm aware of time as some kind of topographical object which I'm able to view all at once, in its entirety. The dinosaurs are over here, right next to Shakespeare and the completed Millennium Dome.

It seems to me that I've suddenly woken up to my original condition; I've always been a higher dimensional fractal froth of thinking quicksilver. So has everyone else. In fact, our physical bodies are all facets of the *same* fractal froth of thinking mercury. Meanwhile, the others are blending with me, constantly exchanging raw information like saliva, asking me where I'd like to go now.

'Alpha Centauri . . .' I suggest, not completely kidding.

Everything around me collapses down into a moving point and suddenly we're in space and there's a big white sun ahead with a smaller one behind it. An enormous dark green planetary horizon is looming up from the right.

'Where next?'

More *Stargate* SFX and I'm being hurried through another world. Crooked tenement buildings crowd together over cobbled fairytale streets. Worn stairs lead into gloomy closes. Everything is all strange curves. Buildings are made of painted enamel like little fishbowl castles grown large enough to house families. It's the town the Seven Dwarfs would plan after Snow White spiked their porridge oats with mescalin; gnomish houses proliferating eerily towards the horizon.

I'm convinced I've accessed a state outside life and time. I've lost contact with the room and Ulric and Kathmandu.

'This reality can penetrate space-time or duplicate space-time but is not contained in space-time . . .'

My rave-blob pals are back. They're sorry to report I won't be able to squeeze many of their concepts back down into 3-D but that I should try to remember as much as I'm able.

The entities – our own 'future' or 'higher' aspects – exist to create and to play and their games involve complete immersion in the gameboard that is our space-time universe. Total identification with any selected gamepiece allows 'them' to experience all the thrills of flesh and pain and time and human emotion.

I'm starting to grasp the concept; our physical bodies are equivalent to computer-game sprites or chess pieces; the entire universe I've grown up in and will die in is a constructed playing field. The super-reality I'm experiencing is simply what you see when you break concentration and look up from the Game.

As a final demonstration, I'm shown how to detach a smaller fractal-foam blob from the substance of my own fluid-mirror 'body'.

The infant blob is holographic, I'm told, and contains the complete informational content of the parent intelligence. It anchors itself into the liquid-information we're swimming through and begins to crackle and fizz at the edges.

I can't imagine how I could have forgotten this. I know what's about to happen. The babyblob's hissing like sherbet, growing and folding up all around until it's everywhere. This is how we start a game and it's time to play again.

My eyes are still open and there's a bolster supporting my neck. I can almost feel the extremities of my body extending out into directions we can't point to in three-dimensional space, but it's only for moments. Kathmandu jigsaws itself together in one awkward instant and I'm back in the world, back in the Game, shaken.

I need to move, to feel the blood thumping and the wet mesh of muscles. I hit my feet and normal consciousness at the same time, staggering across the room, past where Ulric's asleep in the deep of the afternoon. I feel like some bearded starry veck stumbling out of the desert after forty days and nights, mugged by ET, ranting: *Imagination is a fuel!*

'Ulric! I've just had the most amazing thing ever . . .' I croak.

Ulric groans, clutches his gut and rolls on to his side.

I make it to the toilet just in time to jettison gallons of watery shit.

And much to my surprise, as though in an alchemist's crucible, diarrhoea turns to gold.

Further information is available on request.

James Flint
Oh to Play Golf on Mars

Born in Stratford-upon-Avon in 1968, James Flint studied philosophy and music in the UK and the US before moving to London and turning to fiction and journalism. While writing his first novel Habitus (Fourth Estate), he earned his living as an editor on Wired UK. He is currently working on a new book, the story of an artist adrift in one of the nuclear cities at the heart of the United States Cold War atomic weapons programme.

Soft rain of Brussels falling outside, but everything's brown and this was supposed to be a weekend away. Another one. Madeleine lights a cigarette, tiny ashes gather in the folds of her knee-length flower-print dress. She hooks one shoelace strap back up over her shoulder with the hand that holds the lighter. Richard doesn't smoke now.

Downstairs in the foyer groups of retirees on cultural coach tours stand making small talk, comment upon each other's coordinated outfits, soak up the ambience sustained by the myriad faux-Edwardian details – here a moulded light-fitting, there a dado, a picture rail, an Impressionist print carefully screwed to the wall. The staff enjoy their livery of British Racing Green, waistcoats designer-matched with ill-fitting shirts and name tags; behind reception someone dawdles at a keyboard, her fingers delighted with the swift access they've been afforded to the status of every room.

'Do you want to pay for a movie?' Madeleine to Richard, up in their double with bathroom.

'We could. What is there?'

'Don't know. Where's the thing?'

'Er . . . there, over there by the mini-kettle.' Madeleine leans over from the bed, its coverlet a mulch of green and beige, and reaches the leatherette folder containing the hotel information pack from the low wood-effect dresser, her movements languid, without pain. She props her ciggie in the smoked-glass ashtray and flips it open.

'There's *Lethal Weapon 4*. The next one starts in half an hour. Or *Robin Hood: Prince of Thieves* in forty minutes.'

'Christ. That all?'

'*Sleepless in Seattle?*'

'No way. What about the adult channel?'

'You're so fucking predictable.'

'What else is there?'

'Well, we could . . .'

'Maybe later. Maybe in an hour?'

'I fancy a drink.'

'There's some vodka left.'

'Any mixers?'

'Er . . . no. No, we drank all the tonic last night.' Madeleine began to untwine her limbs, stretch out on the bed: 'Richie . . .'

'No way, no – I'm watching the news.'

'How do you know what I'm going to ask?'

'*"Richie, will you go get me some tonic from the bar?"* '

Madeleine laughs, blows smoke at him.

'Well, will you? Go on! Ple-ease. There's nothing on the news anyway.'

'There is. There are pictures due to come in from Mars. From Sojourner. I'm waiting for them.'

'It's only to the bar.'

Richard sighs, gets up and throws a pillow at his wife, negotiates the clothes and luggage they've strewn across the floor and leaves the room. As he walks along the white corridor he watches the hotel logos machined into the carpet flashing underfoot. They're only on the first floor so he doesn't take the lift, takes the stairs instead, passes through the security door at their foot, the very one his magnetic room key/swipe card will open for him on his way back up. He emerges in the Pavilion Suite, a fantasia of bamboo-patterned wallpaper and split-cane chairs set around glass-topped tables with genuine hardwood legs. Behind their Hawaiian fringe of plastic palm fronds the drinks fridges and stainless steel cabinets of the corner bar tremble like the braces of a débutante at the approaching promise of the hotel night, in the deep miracle of which the wordless muzak that is now playing will be replaced by jungle drums and the Pavilion Suite will once more fulfil its destiny and transform itself into the humid terrace at the island retreat of Doctor Moreau.

Richard continues, the brush of his trainers across the artificial fibres of the carpet charging him with an invisible sheen of static electricity. The electrons tremble at his skin like some terrible soapsud as he transits from carpet to tile, from colonial club to Edwardian charm, from incidental cocktail lounge and dayroom to combination foyer/reception. The retirees eye him warily as he crosses before them, their skin more plastic than his, their clothes better-fitting, their internal organs cleansed now of the toxins and residues so attractive to the young. Their creases and wrinkles, so pliant and rehydrated, are an affirmation. In their sensible shoes they stand there, their suitcases standing tidily against the skirting, nicely set off by the striped wallpaper, or set carefully into small clumps with family resemblance, draped with a well-folded rain mac perhaps, handles extended and ready. The retirees are so much more prepared for the world than Richard. And there are so many of them, too. He tries to avoid the placid stares of the women who sit, gloves folded in their laps, smiling at the refit they see before them.

He makes it to the lounge bar, feels it fold around him, its warm embrace carefully distilled from centuries of the very best of Anglo-French traditions. Its mahogany-look partitions and individual spotlights with bell-shaped shades in real glass indicate the English city pub while cleverly hinting in harmonious simultaneity at both the New York cocktail bar and the absinthe-drinkers' den. Richard feels strangely at home, and at the counter his foot finds the brass-look foot-rail of its own, simple accord.

The bar attendant is pretty, and he smiles at her and thinks about her tits. He asks for the tonic and smiles, and she smiles back so he orders himself a beer. Would she like one, too? Ah, no, she can't drink on duty, of course. He flirts, it's a beautiful game, she looks like a catalogue model, and when she leans over the till there's a glimpse of the ribbons of her indigo bra (the one that the manageress has had to speak to her about in the past) between the white buttons of her white serving shirt (while serving in the bar staff are permitted to divest themselves of their waistcoats). Her breasts look big; Richard wants to touch them, he wants that more than anything. He takes the drinks and his change, and he asks her for a box of matches so that she'll turn and he can see her buttocks, thighs and panty-line through the green polyester of her pencil skirt. He goes back upstairs with a hard-on, imagining Madeleine and the girl in a series of positions. Underfoot, the logos slide.

Back in the room, they drink.
  'I wanted a beer!'
  'No you didn't, you wanted a tonic.'
  'But I didn't think of beer.'
  'Well, share mine. I'll get more later. Shall we do the adult channel?'
  'Go on, then.' They do the adult channel. It's better than at home. You see genitals and come-shots. Richard's hard-on comes and goes. He and Madeleine start to touch each other and then gradually forget, distracted by the screen. There's a plot involving a swimming pool and a hotel room, better than the one they're in.
  'If we had more money do you think we'd have better sex?'
  'No, darling, we have the best sex already.' Reassuring – but genuine, too.
  'No, but would we? I mean, if we could be in a nicer hotel than this, by the sea, with palm trees and sun.' It occurred to Richard that if he could have just that with just those elements, that Madeleine might not fit. He looked at her in her print dress, her body slightly wrong. How was that? He thought about the bar attendant.
  'Do you want a beer, then?'
  'It's all right, love, you don't need to go down again.'
  'No, it's OK, I don't mind. I want another one anyway. D'you want anything to eat while I'm at it?'

'Erm, peanuts? No . . . cashews.'
'Okey-dokey. See you in a minute.'

Over the logos and down the stairs, penis stiff in his pocket.
The retirees are leaving, Richard can see them just beyond
the hotel's front doors, overseeing the stowing of their
luggage into the bays of their coach. Many of them are
wearing their macs. Some sports caps or headscarves as
well. One or two of the frailer ladies wait inside, out of the
rain, waiting for their chipper husbands – steaming slightly
from their exertions, raindrops beading on the rogue fibres of
their scarlet Pringle V-necks – to return and fetch them.
Richard slips past and into the bar, but the pretty attendant is
no longer on duty and the place seems less accommodating
now. Richard orders two beers from the small and neat
barman (who has opted to keep wearing his waistcoat
during his shift) and quickly returns to Madeleine and their
room.

'Shit, I forgot the nuts.'
'Oh, it's all right. I think there's some in the minibar.' The
adult channel continues with a different film, a platinum
blonde getting fucked in furs in a skiing lodge. Richard wants
her. He takes his cock out and pulls Madeleine's head down
on to it. She complies.

Afterwards, still fully clothed, Richard looks out of the
window.

'Maybe we should go out.'
'Oh, I couldn't, I'm still too fucked from last night. Anyway,
it's horrible. Look at it.' Outside, the rain turns the city – its
pavements, its trees – to metal and plastic. 'There's not even
any wind. It would be all right if it was a proper storm.'
'Maybe there's a nice café we could go to. We could go
back to that one we went to yesterday.'
'What, where we had tea?'
'Mmm. Their hot chocolate was *so* good.'
'We could.'

'Wasn't that odd, seeing Willem Dafoe in the street like that?' This had happened to them the previous day as they were stepping out for the evening, first to dinner (Indonesian rice-table) and then to a show (partial striptease and simulated sex).

'I *know*. He looked straight at us. Where do you think he's staying?'

'Not here.' Richard looks across at Madeleine, sprawled on the bed. The strap has slipped off her shoulder again. Why can't she be neater? Perhaps he should have married a lap-dancer or a newscaster. He stares at his feet, at his suede slip-ons, light tan. At the ironed slacks he wears, at the short-sleeved shirt of blue Nicaraguan cotton.

'I think I'm turning into my father.'

'Don't be silly.'

'Look at me. Look at my clothes. All I need's a cravat.'

'But your clothes are nice!'

'That's what worries me.'

'Well, I find you attractive. And, anyway, I quite fancy your Dad.'

'Christ.' Richard lies back on the bed and stares up at the ceiling, seeing in the fire-resistant polystyrene tiles an endless procession of three-star hotel rooms, of well-fitting clothes, of mild intoxication and light conversation, of unattainable bar girls juxtapositioned with marital sex, of amusements and airports and items of luggage with trolleys built in. He has a vision of weekend breaks with vodka and tonics, of a life spent reading brochures and catalogues, of executive services and corporate hospitality, of circulating through Europe on one endless deductible junket.

Another adult movie begins: Tanya and Deborah after hours at the gym. He watches it while Madeleine flicks through a magazine. Tanya lies spread-eagled on the bench-press. He notices that her legs are too fat, that her belly is tired, that her make-up's too thick. This complicates things. He changes the channel.

*

Richard watches CNN. The pictures arrive from Mars. He thinks about hitting balls down a fairway, of the crunch of spiked shoes on perfectly mown greens, of the beauty and regularity of machine-moulded balls that fit in the hand just so, of the perfection of motion, a modern t'ai chi. The newscaster is attractive. She resembles the bar attendant. She tells Richard that US forces may bomb Iraq, that golf clubs are tax-free to foreigners, that heroin kills.

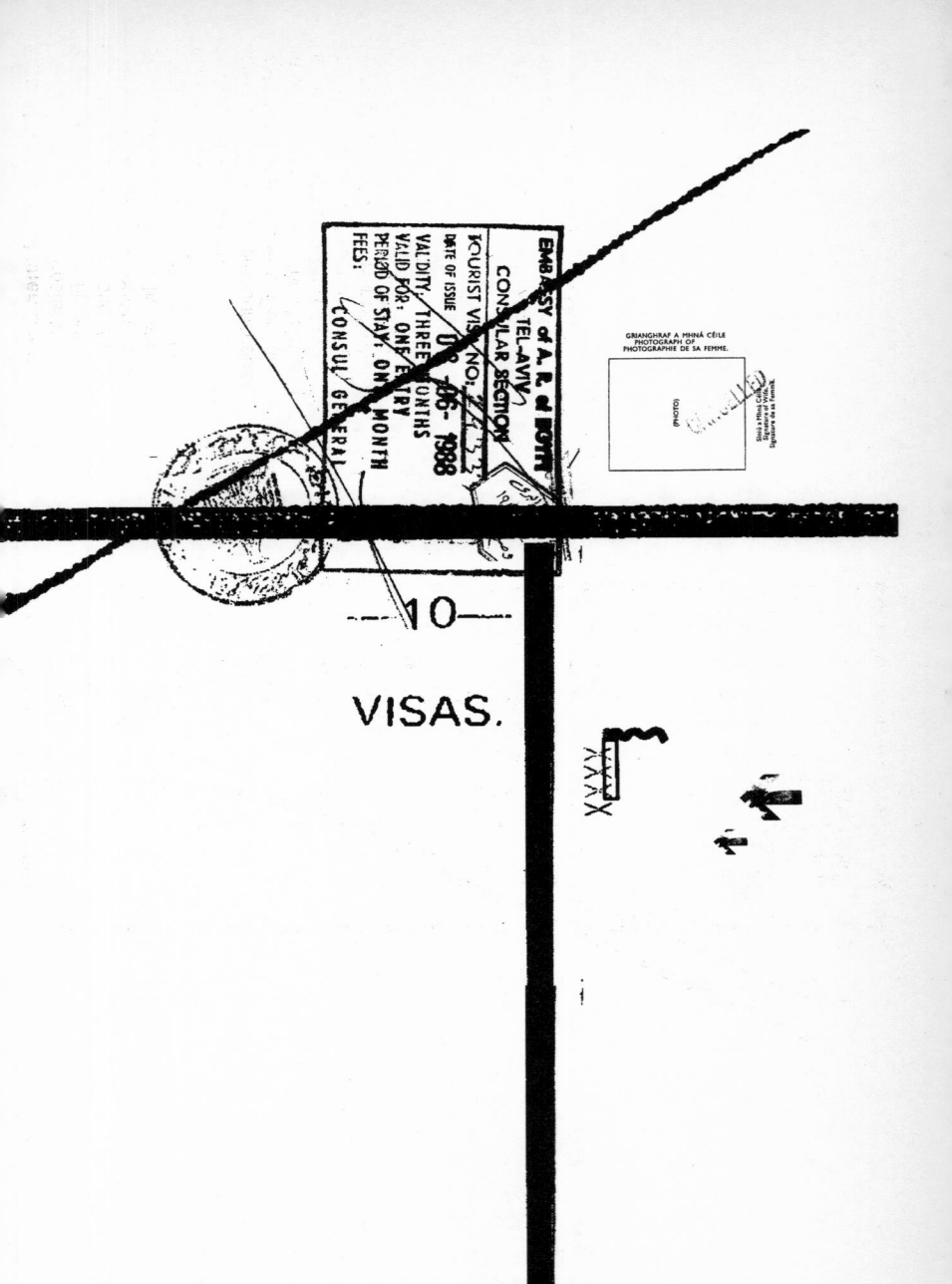

--10--

VISAS.

EMBASSY of A. R. of ROM
TEL-AVIV
CONSULAR SECTION
TOURIST VISA NO.
DATE OF ISSUE
VALIDITY: THREE MONTHS
VALID FOR: ONE ENTRY
PERIOD OF STAY: ONE MONTH
FEES:
CONSUL GENERAL

GRIANGHRAF A MHNÁ CÉILE
PHOTOGRAPH OF
PHOTOGRAPHIE DE SA FEMME.

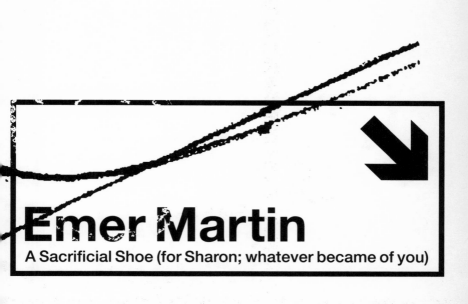

Emer Martin

A Sacrificial Shoe (for Sharon; whatever became of you)

Emer Martin is a Dubliner. She has lived in Paris, London, Amsterdam, Israel, Savannah and San Francisco, and now resides in New York. She suffers from a medical condition called CAT (Compulsive Aimless Travelling). There is no known cure. Symptoms include suddenly finding yourself transported from certain bars on the Lower East Side to unpronounceable destinations in Africa, Asia, Central America, Indonesia and the Caribbean. Her first novel Breakfast In Babylon won Ireland's Book of the Year at the 1996 Listowel Writers' Week. Her novella Teeth Shall be Provided was part of

Rebel Inc's Rovers Return collection. More Bread or I'll Appear, her second novel, was published in the US in

As long as I can remember I have been waiting for both my parents to die so that I can commit suicide. At the bottom of the ocean water bubbled into my nose and my arms groped vainly like defeathered wings. With a last surge of energy my head broke the surface and I gulped for air, but the waves splashed into my lungs, filling me up, pulling me down again. I was spinning, swallowing and grasping. Then I felt a hand on my ankle and I glimpsed her big body, her skimpy neon-green bikini, her pudgy claws hooking me toward her. I thought she was messing and didn't know I was drowning. I tried to wriggle away but she pulled me by the foot. I was eating the sea, chomping big bites of salty, vomity water. Was she trying to kill me? Her finger pulled lightly at the strap of my sandal and casually undid the buckle, flipping the shoe into the sea. What *was* she doing? At that instant of surprise and rage, I drowned.

Sharon had disgusted me from the moment I saw her stride into the kibbutz dining room. There had been a new batch of volunteers arriving, and since us lot had all slept with each other, fought, broke up, switched alignments and betrayed allegiances, we were eager to assess and initiate this new bunch. That particular morning was that time of the year when a siren sounds all over the country and every Israeli freezes exactly where they are and stands for three minutes' silence in remembrance of Holocaust victims. It is a stunning nationwide performance: cars stop in the street, children's swings pause in suspension. In the dining room I heard the siren wail. All the workers halted in mid-motion as if they were in a science-fiction movie. I froze holding a saucepan with a dish-towel. I was thoroughly enjoying the drama, the sense of unity, the sheer theatre of it all, when she strode in – an eighteen-year-old fat slob in a tight T-shirt, tiny bum-hugging shorts, with curly blonde hair. She stomped through us, and in a thick Scottish accent said, 'What's this? The breakfast siren?' Then she grabbed a plate and proceeded to slop the buffet breakfast on to her dish. Not even questioning why we were all motionless snapshots of ourselves. Not feeling how appalled the Jews were. She was the crude spell-breaker who had reduced us to mere chess pieces waxed to the board.

Sharon made us all cringe because she was fat yet wore tight clothes. Because she fucked all the soldiers and Arab farm-workers, and drove a tractor across the manicured lawn. Because she belly-flopped with a roar into the pool on top of the children. Because of the way she shovelled food into herself, sometimes pushing bread into her already stuffed mouth with her finger, like those guys with white gloves in Tokyo pushing commuters into the subway trains.

She was like a savage child raised by wolves except she was raised by nothing at all. Her mother had been a junkie whore in the Edinburgh slums and eventually Sharon was put into care. Despite the misery of her life, and the fact that she could barely read or write, she had the audacity to be permanently jolly and indiscriminately friendly.

I on the other hand had it all. I was tall and slim with long sandy straight hair. I was from a privileged Protestant background in South Dublin. Sharon and I had just one thing in common; neither of us had any brothers or sisters.

Everyone wanted to work outside. That was the point of being on a kibbutz. I had been stuck on dining-room duty for a month, so I complained. We gathered around a big chart every week to see our assigned duties. They had sent me to the chickens – better than the laundry, I suppose, but I had been hoping for the orchards. To my dismay Sharon and Sandy had been assigned to work with me. Sandy was a Scottish girl who had arrived with Sharon. She was also blonde but plain and washed-out, quiet to the point of

muteness. She had one of those faces that had probably
looked haggard and drawn since she was four. They had met
in the orphanage and were like sisters. Sandy was Sharon's
shadow and I never heard her speak a word unless she was
called upon to do so.

The three of us stood amidst a white sea of chickens. Our
job was to pick them up and put them in cages. The farmer
told us to scoop them up by the feet and carry three at a time
in each hand. Sometimes their feet would come off. They
were so tightly packed in that if one chicken was injured the
others would start pecking at its wound and tear it apart.
About midday, I sent Sharon off to get us lunch. Sandy and I
ploughed along grabbing chickens and kicking chickens
aside. Sharon came back, wading through the bobbing birds.
We wiped our hands on our overalls and took the
sandwiches she offered.

'Aggh!' I yelled, spitting out my half-chewed food on top of
a few chickens that pecked and devoured it off the other
chickens' backs. Sharon hooted with laughter, slapping her
thigh. Sandy opened the bread, inspected the contents and
said the first words I had ever heard her speak. 'Egg salad,
for fuck's sake, Sharon!'

Suddenly the farmer ran in shouting. 'Wild cats! Come from
desert. Quick, hurry!' We ran after him. Stray cats would
often stalk the chickens outside the sheds. I always felt sorry
for those escaped chickens, the intrepid few who would
wander from the chicken hell inside. Pathetically, they never
went far. You never saw a lone chicken walk off into the
desert to live the life of the rugged individualist; rather, they
remained pecking around outside the sheds in small, errant
groups, resigned to their miserable poultry fate. Now the cats
I could respect. For they had wandered away from their
saucers of milk and flea-collars and had learned to breed in
the desert and become a menace to their former masters.
Workers were throwing rocks at the cats. We cornered a
ginger one, and I fired a stone with such force that the cat's
head exploded on impact. It gave me a taste for it; I soaked

up the cheers and went for another. Sharon and Sandy stood
by with their rocks in their hands and watched. Nobody really
expected women to do that kind of work anyway. I was
making a point.

'Hey, Avril,' Sharon said to me after all the cats had
retreated back to the desert, or lay wounded or dead on the
ground. 'Let him without sin cast the first stone.'

'That would be me.' I told her coldly as I lit a cigarette with
shaking hands. The farmer patted me on the shoulder, 'Good
work, Avril.' The Arab workers looked at me a little funny.
They talked among themselves and laughed while still staring
at me. I gave them the finger and walked back to the awful
white sea of doomed chickens.

Mostly it was Sharon's stupidity that annoyed me. Really, I
can forgive any sin but stupidity. Her primitive practical jokes
were invariably followed by loud self-congratulatory guffaws
of laughter. She knew nothing about anything, she was
ignorant, she ate all the time, and she picked her nose. She
was too fat. She was prone to crass and tasteless
utterances. One day I was taking a shower and she came up
beside me. I was naked and she looked me up and down
appraisingly.

'You're so thin, Avril, you're emancipated.'

'Emaciated.' I corrected her, wincing. I did not like her
unsubtle inspection of my body. There was an unspoken
code in the communal showers that she had just violated.

Before she turned on the water she looked up into the
shower nozzle and said with a snort, 'I half-expect gas to
come out, don't you?'

'I'm surprised you've even heard of the Holocaust.'

'Uri told me about it just last week.'

'You've been with Uri the soldier?'

I had been chubby as a teenager but had stumbled on
heroin in Dublin bars in my late teens. Beauty secret #1, I
called it. I got thin on it. It was only ten quid a bag then and
cheaper than drinking. Everyone was doing it. Especially the
upper-middle-class kids I hung out with. Most of us ended up

with nasty habits. The whole junkie bonanza came to an
abrupt end when I OD'd at my cousin's wedding in the
bathrooms of the Killiney Court Hotel. My parents freaked
out. So after a costly stint at the private Rutland rehab, I
came over to Israel in an attempt to keep away from the old
crowd. Now I lived in fear of getting fat again, and here was
Sharon, grotesquely naked, casting judgements on my
physique, slapping about in the water, soaping the crack of
her flabby arse with undue vigour. Her fish-white body was
unevenly patched with red sunburn. Without warning, she
started to shave her pussy. I nearly gagged.

'Do you have to do that here?'

'What do you care? You want tae check it oot? Are you a
lezzer? A carpet-muncher? Do I turn you on?' She danced
about in the shower, and Sandy came in and sprayed some
shaving-cream on Sharon's crotch and they squealed with
delight. Disgusted, I went to the bench to put my clothes on.
Sharon came running out to inspect her new state in the
mirror. Sandy followed, similarly deplumed.

'Ooo, sexy, huh? Wait till Uri sees us.'

I couldn't help looking at her labia; they were giant, the
Dumbo the elephant of labia. She caught my glance and
winked. When they were gone I looked in the mirror. I had
been more or less clean for a year. Beauty secret #1 had
done wonders for my body, given it that lean muscled look,
but it had begun to ravage my face. I guess I should have
spared a thought for Keith Richards and Iggy Pop before I
embarked on my quest for physical perfection.

Every Friday night there was a disco in a shed. It was just
for the volunteers and the soldiers. The normal kibbutzim and
the young Jewish-American kids wouldn't come near us. We
were unclean in that way. They considered us all trouble-
makers, alcoholics and drug addicts. They commented that
our laundry was the filthiest, and maybe they were right, but
we were given the filthiest jobs. I think they held the
Palestinian workers in higher regard than they held us. In fact
I know they did. We were so bored at night on the kibbutz

that Friday was an excuse to go mental. The Argentinian
volunteers were headbanging to 'La Bamba'. It was the third
time they had insisted it be played that night. I was speaking
to Uri, or rather hissing at him, 'How could you?'

'What do you care?'

Young soldiers danced in their khakis. They were stationed
here for part of their military service. Perhaps because of their
youth, and the fact that they too were far from their families,
they were the only Israelis who would come near us. They
also came to fuck us, since they couldn't do the kibbutz girls.
I obliged but kept it low key. The other volunteers were wary
of the soldiers – their guns, aggression and boasts of Arab-
beatings. As a signal to Uri I wore a leather belt to the disco
every Friday. Uri was the usual DJ. The soldiers loved U2.
They would go as wild as the Argentinians for 'La Bamba'
when they played 'Sunday Bloody Sunday', fists in the air,
roaring the words, loving the blood in the title.

Uri pulled me by the belt to him. He fingered the pocked
leather – pocked by his own teeth-marks. I would get him to
take me out to the fields and choke me until I came. It was
the only way I could do it. I never let on to the other
volunteers, as I was well respected among them for being
cool and quite elegant. Uri once tried to take me to his bed
and give me flowers, but I practically spat at him. I needed
him for one thing only, and he was an eager, if not entirely
committed sadist. I'm what's known as a pushy bottom. I
demand my abuse. Now I could never go near him again
because of her.

Pissed off, I borrowed a bicycle that was lying outside and
pedalled furiously to the silicone factory at the gate of the
kibbutz. The factory manufactured condoms and rubber
gloves. I cycled over the dirt to the back of the big building.
The sky was littered with a dandruff of stars. I longed to brush
them away so that things could be clear. The casts for the
gloves and condoms were outside, rows and rows on
shelves. A thousand hands and penises grasping.

I was obliged to choke myself from then on. Luckily, I had

my own room; the only volunteer to do so. I had managed to get rid of all my room-mates and not have them replaced by the new batches constantly arriving. Tying my belt to the iron foot of the bed, I lay on the dusty floor and pushed my feet against the wall. Sometimes I yanked so hard the bed would screech across the floor, sounding like a slaughtered animal.

When I was dying in the sea, she saved me. She pulled me out of the whirlpool by my leg. She put her mouth to mine on the beach and blew life into me. Everyone was gathered around to witness this. Finally, I stood up gasping. I pushed through the crowd and ran back to the water.

'I lost my shoe,' I cried out and tried to return to the ocean. The others laughed and pulled me back. It was only a plastic shoe, a blue jelly sandal. The kibbutz gave them to us free along with our boots and overalls. But the volunteer trip would last another day and I would be barefoot in Akra. The dirty donkey-shit streets. There seemed to be something wrong with the eyes of the Arabs there, all cataracts, phlegm, glazed and bloodshot. Meat hung in open windows, black with flies.

A donkey had a fit. It lay on its side and flipped about, its hairy, speckled, gummy mouth foaming, its side ripped until it made butterfly swishes in blood on the ground. A cloud of brown dust created by its seizure settled on me, beading my eyelashes, coating my sweaty neck and chest. I could taste it.

And I was barefoot amidst all this.

We had all slept on the beach the night before. Many people had had trouble in the water. Several of our group were scratched and torn. Sharon had saved us all. She had been a lifeguard back in Scotland. Now she had plucked us all out of the sea. Everyone loved her from then on. I couldn't bear it. That night I couldn't sleep. Like Lazarus, I sat on the shore and looked into the deep shock of sea for my one shoe. In the morning, as everyone made breakfast over a fire, they sniggered as I scoured the sand on the off chance that my plastic shoe had been washed ashore.

At last they put me working in the orchard, but I found no solace there. I was thinking of Sharon, now beloved, and the ungenerous sea. Finally, I phoned my parents and told them I was leaving the kibbutz. I was going to try my luck in Tel Aviv instead. As usual they worried. They offered to send money but I refused. They suggested I come back and finish college and settle down a bit. I wished they had had another child. I knew I was not going back. I did not want to belong anywhere. I needed to be separate from the community, to scour the margins as an outsider. I would live abroad in non-Western cultures until my parents died, and then I would be free to hang myself. That had always been the plan. Lying in my bed beneath pop-star posters, counting the days to their cancers and heart attacks and lightning strikes on the golf course. By now the rope's grip was so familiar that when death came it would be an old friend.

Maybe that's why I liked Israel; there was a war.

When I saw children with stones face down soldiers with guns it felt just like home. I had started college in Queen's University in Belfast. A southern Anglican Protestant among northern Presbyterians and Catholics, studying architecture in a place where they love to blow up buildings. Eventually, I went back to Dublin for the drugs. Couldn't find any in Belfast. It was a police state, what with all the Brits and the paramilitaries. No place for an addict like me, and I was in deep at that stage.

Predictably, we annihilated ourselves at my going-away party. Someone whispered the vicious rumour that Sharon had gang-banged the Palestinian farmhands. That shocked the crowd. Secretly, I exulted. Later, she came sweeping into our midst with Uri and his machine gun, Sandy trailing after her like a dog. Of course, she was oblivious to any dirty looks. I had a sudden vision of her grabbing Uri's dark head in her giant Dumbo the Elephant labia and squeezing his skull until his brain popped out of his head, like pus from a pimple.

Everyone was at work when I took the bus out of the sheltered kibbutz life. Oddly enough, I would miss the volunteers. Strange bonds inevitably arose from the grim combination of boredom and enforced proximity. Only Sharon and Sandy took time out to come and wave goodbye. I tensed when Sharon hugged me, but since she had saved my life I could hardly push her away.

'So you're not working with the chickens any more?'

'No, we like the factory work.'

'What on earth do they have you doing in the condom factory? Quality control?'

She laughed heartily at this. 'We do like to be around all them cocks, don't we, Sandy?'

Sandy half-smiled. I stuck out my hand, and I could almost swear the little bitch hesitated before taking it.

'Ah, go on. Give each other a hug, would ye.' Sharon pushed us together but we both recoiled like charged magnets.

'You know what's wrong with you, Sharon?' I told her, casually inspecting my self-manicured nails, as the bus pulled into the clearing. 'You're a great person with a shite personality.'

She was crestfallen as I staggered aboard with my bag on my back but she still managed to wave bravely as Sandy took her hand and led her away.

Under the water the last day of my life replayed in backward sequence. I had gone for a swim with the group from the kibbutz and the waves had looked so enticing at first. I was only a few metres from the shore, and I decided to wade out to dry land again. Foolishly, I turned my back to the sea. This was my mistake. WHOMP! The thunder of the waves flipped me, again and again. WHOMP! I was trying to walk towards the shore but instead was being pulled in a diagonal undertow right into a whirlpool by the rocks. All I could think of was that my parents would be told that I had drowned on some kibbutz outing by the Lebanese border. That would be the end of the only life they had managed to squeeze into the universe. This was the pressure of the only child. They should have had one more – a spare.

284 : **Fortune Hotel**

On the way to the beach we had stopped the bus to listen to the distant rumble of bombs, like the good tourists we were. Fingers itching on cameras – but you can't photograph the sound of war or its particular treacherous monotony. The sound excited us. It was as if all there were to it were the sounds in the bare air and not the buildings collapsing or the children running in the roads, ripped and bloody from them. Earlier in the day we had gone for a hike, and as I scampered nimbly up the side of a mountain like a goat, Sharon had huffed and puffed way down below, Sandy giving her a hand every now and then.

'You have great stanima,' she told me when we were all at the top and she had extracted chocolate from her bag and was handing it around.

'Stamina,' I said, coldly refusing her sweaty square of mushy chocolate. 'Maybe if you didn't stuff your face so much you would be able to move better.'

'Avril.' Everyone shouted in unison, but I could see they were amused. Later, in the sea, she would bother to save my life. She could have just saved the others and pretended to be unable to reach me. I'm sure everyone would have understood. But she did take off my shoe. It was very deliberate. I couldn't find it in my heart to forgive her that. I questioned her about it and she just shrugged.

'I can't believe you're denying it. You undid the buckle and everything.'

The others ridiculed my monomania. All the way south on the bus I persisted.

'Leave off it, Avril,' they told me. 'It's just a lousy shoe. It wasn't even yours. She saved your fucking life. She saved us all.'

The Israel outside the kibbutz was a shock to my system. At first, I worked as a dish-washer in Tel Aviv. The boss made a pass at me late at night when I was cleaning the toilets. I poked him in the groin with my mop and he fired me without pay. Then I was working in a bar in a brothel on the sea front. The whores were mainly transvestites and really bad ones at that. Big hairy lummoxes of men in floral dresses and granny handbags. Plenty of Irish soldier clients down from the Lebanon. It was a long time since I had met Irish people. I was excited at first.

'Where are you from in Dublin?' I asked a table of soldiers.

'Ballymun, and you?'

'Foxrock.'

'That's not Dublin that's fucking Wicklow,' one waved his hands dismissively.

'I used to rob houses out there,' another said, and they all hooted at his witticism. I gave up the foolish bonding ritual.

My only company was the old man who rented the few rooms out over his shop. He had camp numbers tattooed on his arm, and he lived modestly in one room. 'The chosen people,' he would say. 'I went to Tahiti. What a lovely place! They're the chosen people most likely. Why the hell do we think we're the chosen people, sitting surrounded by five hostile Arab nations?' We used to sit on his bed and watch old Cary Grant movies. We were both in love with Cary Grant. I never asked him, but once he pointed to the numbers and I enquired as to which camp. As if I knew the difference.

'I put it on myself so they would feel sorry for me. It is a mark of pride in Israel.'

'Jesus,' I smiled, assuming he was joking.

'Why do they hate Jews? Can you tell me that? They say we control the banks, a world-wide Jewish conspiracy. Where do I come in, then? I'm a Jew. Where's my monthly cheque?'

'I think you were never forgiven for not wanting to become us.'

Seven nights a week I worked, and he always gave me free fresh fruit from the shop and cans of beer at 5 a.m. when I came stumbling in. That was when we'd watch the videos. Either he was quite the early riser or he never slept at all. We formed a bond, he and I, he damaged by history and I by discarded privilege. This gloomy routine didn't last. The old man was excited to tell me that my friends had arrived and

were in the room beside me. Sickened, I knew immediately.
Who else would claim to be my friends? Sharon had been
thrown off the kibbutz for setting a peanut field on fire: 'Me
and Sandy were told to set fire to a bunch of dry sticks in the
desert by the orchard. We poured petrol over them but they
wouldnae light. So we poured more and more. 'Magine not
being able to light a bunch of dry sticks covered in petrol in
the desert. Well, finally when we got it going, it set fire to the
field beside it and all. Roasted bloody peanuts! It was fucken
mental. The guy in the post room said you gave this
forwarding address. Great, isn't it? Me an' Sandy said, we'll
go up there an play wee Avril a visit.'

It was a weird obligation I felt to Sharon. I had to even out
the score. I didn't like owing anything to anybody. I couldn't
even bear owing life to my parents for Christ's sake. I
resented them for me. The way they created me and no one
else. As if I would suffice for future generations. Sharon got
terribly sunburnt at the beach on the first day. Yellow blisters
the size of orange segments clustered on her shoulders. She
handed me the cream and wanted me to rub it on her.

'Can't do it, Sharon.'

'Och, please, Avril, it hurts.'

'No. Where's Sandy?'

'She's oot.'

'Oot?'

'Oot looking for a job.'

Squeezing the cream on to my hands I sat behind her
naked crispy mountain of a body, my hands poised to touch,
but I faltered. 'I can't, Sharon. Fuck it. You're too disgusting.'
It would have to be something else.

The ugly trannies gave me the boot at work because of
her. She and Sandy would show up and fuck the customers
for free. The old man was concerned for us all as we headed
to Jerusalem to try our luck there.

'Watch out,' he said. 'Jerusalem is full of fanatics. And if
you go to the West Bank, stay away from those settlers.
They're all wackos.' We did go to Bethlehem. Sharon and

Sandy wanted to see where Jesus was born. I think they actually believed the whole story. Although they both believed in reincarnation, too. In fact, they believed in everything.

'In my last life I might have been buried alive,' Sharon said to us on the bus.

'Why?' Sandy asked.

' 'Cos I'm so afraid of small spaces. I go a wee bit daft. Closetphobic,' she said in earnest. 'And in the life before that . . .'

'Please,' I interrupted before this inanity went any further. 'I'm not even interested in your present life, don't bore me with your past ones.'

Bethlehem was under a curfew. Soldiers on the road told us we could not enter the town. We sat and waited by Rachel's tomb until they had gone, and then we walked into the square. Nervous soldiers peered from around corners, their guns pointed. Warily, we entered the Church of the Nativity.

'The wee mon was born here,' Sharon said in awe. She and Sandy held hands and genuflected.

'Are you Catholics?' I asked, amused.

'We don't know. We were in the home. No one telt us.'

'It makes nae odds.' Sandy put her arm around Sharon.

'No one told you what God you belonged to? Lucky you,' I said. They looked rather sad at this. Orphans in every way.

'You must be Catholic if you're Irish.'

'Wrong as usual. This is run by the Greek Orthodox anyway. I remember being shocked to think there were Christians who were not Catholic or Protestant.' At the altar there were stairs to a room below. Supposedly the very manger in which Jesus was born. We descended, and to our surprise there was a bearded Greek Orthodox priest sitting on a chair with a Band-Aid on his nose. He was eating a banana. He looked at us and Sharon let out a massive fart. Scurrying upstairs, we dashed out of the church and back into the war.

I hadn't found anyone to choke me in a long time, but I'd stopped choking myself – then again, I'd stopped coming too. The three of us worked in a Jerusalem hostel and shared a mattress on the roof. The Yemenite Jew who owned the place came up the ladder one night and gave me a gun.

'You must shoot intruders.'

His mother had carried him in her belly when she was thirteen years old. She had walked through the desert to Israel. When she came to see him she sniffed at us, and I knew she thought we were whores and tramps. Her assumptions did not bother me; in fact, why in hell Sharon and Sandy didn't charge I never knew. They weren't exactly discriminating. Once his mother came over to watch the Eurovision song contest. Everyone in the Middle East seemed to adore this show. The point-scoring was always so nationalistic. In Ireland, when we were growing up, we would wait to see how much the English gave us. When they gave us decent marks we would be convinced they were trying to outsmart us. 'For the Arab countries the fact that Israel can be part of the contest stings,' the boss told us. 'When Israel plays they switch to other programming, and they blot out our name on the scoreboard. They want to pretend we don't exist.' His mother shushed him vehemently – a Finnish trio was leaping about like a bunch of sad jerks, and she was enthralled. She was only thirteen years older than her son.

A Palestinian came in to do the accounts for the hostel. 'Our Israeli Arabs are the best-educated Arabs in the world,' the boss boasted, slapping the accountant on the back. When he left the room the accountant asked me if I was Jewish. I said no, and he said, 'Good. I hate Jews.' I had to give the gun back to the boss. At nights I would lie on the edge of the mattress with Sharon snoring beside me and Sandy on the other side of Sharon, their puppet bodies jerking periodically, tied to the twitching darkness. I held the gun close to my temple. I pushed it through my hair and licked the barrel. When I gave it back I said to him, 'I'm only going to shoot myself.'

I should have shot him. The little creep had a peep-hole straight into the girls' bathroom and another into the all-female dormitory. The treacherous accountant used to look with him. I should have shot them both. Once I woke up with the boss's head between my legs, which Sharon and Sandy thought highly amusing.

I began to think Sharon had a light inside her. I could feel her halo singe my own hair as we tossed on the roof, open to the stars. We used to joke that our mattress was a raft and we were drifting on the sea and the stars were fish. We were hungry for them, and we would reach our arms in the air to reel them in. Sharon had the soul of a jungle orchid: a beautiful thing in a horrible place. She never said a bad word about anything or anyone. She never complained. She gave everything away and shared the nothing she had. She would give you her last tampon and trail blood on the streets. Her vulgarity began to seem like innocence, her farting, burping, stinking and semi-nudity, mere natural states. I would catch her smiling to herself, her face private but shining with some small personal triumph, and it would unnerve me. How could she have salvaged such glowing memories from her murky Edinburgh childhood? In the end I did both their work. They were the laziest, worst workers imaginable. I cleaned the dormitories and bathrooms that they were supposed to do. I took on their breakfast duties while they lay on the unsheltered roof, hung-over and sweating in the grisly sun. At the train station I hustled backpackers, just to let the boss think Sharon and Sandy were down there, pulling their weight and filling the hostel. In truth they did nothing but find men to fuck. Insatiable, voracious, pure cunts that they were.

One time I was drunk and going to meet them in the old city. I fell beside the Damascus Gate, landing right on my face, chipping my tooth. I sat in Sharon's arms and wept, and she cradled and cooed and mopped my stony wounds with Scotch. Brittle and waferish, I dissolved in her great

Buddha embrace. She rocked me, and I asked her why she had to give my shoe to the sea, but she just looked baffled and said, 'Shh! S'awright! S'awright!'

Gradually, I began to detect a certain loss of angularity on my part. Not all the vertebrae were as readable as before. My legs had once been so thin I could plait them about each other. To keep my weight down I had been puking after most meals. After all, it is better to be a bulimic than an anorexic – at least you get to eat the food. One evening Sharon and Sandy said they knew what I was up to. I squirmed and blushed, going over to the edge of the roof, looking at the long fall. Sharon came to me and put her meaty paw on my shoulder. I shrugged her off.

'Avril, you are what you eat, you ken? And if you're puking that up then you must be, eh, like rejecting who you are.' Sandy nodded vigorously.

'Rejecting, is it? That's a word outside your usual five-hundred-word vocabulary. You must be fucking someone smart these days for a change.'

I couldn't bear them knowing that about me. I travelled to erase myself. The sights were duties, an empty parade of mountains, lakes, cities and ruins. What I sought was my own removal from the social mechanism and this I achieved by remaining a perpetual stranger. How I buckled under the tyranny of the quotidian. For these two awful people suddenly to see inside of me, to pierce my exoskeleton of calm nonchalance and know my mushy, boneless interior. What was I doing with these low-class slags, falling on my teeth in Jerusalem? Under the heavy night in that holy city of hate, I packed and slipped away without a trace.

As I dozed in the bus station I was reborn – historyless, unreadable. By disappearing I was self-preserving. I knew they would be fired without me. They were lazy bitches. They, too, would move on. And I would be a ghost in another culture.

Sleeping the next night on disputed territory, I woke up and walked into Egypt. In the Sinai desert I slept for days in a straw hut in a bedouin village and smoked their hash in the

dark dirt sand. I entered the ocean and snorkelled with
strange fish. Their lips were purple, their backs were spotted,
and they glowed and ate eggs from my hands. On the
second week I rode into the desert on a camel with some
Bedouins, and they cooked me bread on the side of metal
scrap. The desert was mined. Some bombs were from the
Second World War, some from more recent wars. Every year,
the Bedouins told me, they lost legs and lives to the poisoned
ground. The earth raged up against them, swallowing their
limbs. They were a people still dying from the Second World
War, or from which war they couldn't tell. War has no end, no
beginning. There is just one war, waged globally for eternity,
the war against our selves, self-loathing projected on to other
tribes.

I climbed Mount Sinai and ate cake on the walls of
St Catherine, where the monks piled their bones in dry
rooms. I floated in a felucca down the Nile and we had to
light little fires in plastic tubs and float them out to the big
Murder on the Nile boats so we would not be mowed down
in the inky African river at night. I hooked up with budget
backpackers on roads lined with sphinxes and I got drunk
and swapped endless adventures in tacky nightclubs down
the backstreets of unpaved towns.

In Alexandria I stayed with an Egyptian family who hired
me to teach English to their sons and daughters. The beach
was crowded with chairs and picnic coolers and women in
black veils. Boys and men danced in the water, frolicking in
skimpy Speedos while the women paddled enviously, their
black robes soaked at the hems, clinging wet about their
ankles.

'Ten years ago women swim in swimsuits but not now,' the
daughter confided. 'Now so many veils. They tell us they will
throw acid in our face if we don't wear them. But foreigner
can swim if go far from men.'

I shook my head. But they inserted me in a black inner
tube, and the lifeguard dragged me out past the crowded
shore and left me in the sea alone. I bobbed about off the

coast of Africa watching humans the size of ants and listening
to their muffled insect-cries of joy. Those cries sounded so
solemn, I almost wept. Would he ever come back for me, and
if he didn't would anyone ever know where I finally sank from
life? My parents would grieve, and I couldn't stand the
thought of their messy mourning, their clumsy, ordinary,
understandable pain. If only they had had another child. It
was their own fault. Their responsibility, not mine. They were
the only people who would ever care, without them I would
be free. No one would miss me if I just stretched my arms to
the sky and slithered from the tube. But the lifeguard broke
away from the coast and scooted out to me on his surfboard.
Reluctantly, I was dragged back to the throng.

While in Alexandria I saw a four-year-old girl covered
entirely in black. A cloth grille was over her eyes and she
wore gloves. It reminded me of home.

Fever struck me, and I went back to Israel, immediately
boarding the wrong bus and ending up in Gaza. Everyone
emptied out into their stateless, conquered lives while the bus
driver fed me beer. Quite drunk and ill, I realized I was the
only passenger left.

'Where are we?' I asked.

'These are orange groves. Next stop my house. Tonight we
go dancing in Gaza.'

'Fuck off!' I struggled off the bus, and he threw my
backpack on to the road at me. 'Where's Israel?' I pleaded.

'There is no such thing as Israel.' he fumed.

I turned and saw an army encampment in the distance,
and I began to walk towards the familiar blue-and-white flag.
The soldiers were waving at me. I waved back, glad to see
them so hospitable. They waved and waved. I had my
Walkman glued to my ears, listening to a Bee Gees tape that
I had swiped from the Egyptian family.

What are you doing in your bed?
You should be dancing, yeah,
Dancing, yeah!

On arriving, grinning, among the soldiers, they tore off
my earphones and spun me around. There were warning
signs for mines all over the field. 'Disco is dangerous.' I told
them.

There are no separate ways, just one endless road; no new
cities, only one city, one mountain, one ocean, one field, one
forest; eternal, universal, inescapable. No peace but one long
war. No two lives but one solitary soul. And if we ever had
reeled those stars in they wouldn't have warmed us; they're
dead things crowding the sky. By the time we acknowledge
their light they're long gone.

   A year later I prepared to leave Israel. The war was still on.
Three hundred years ago in Ireland they had planted a
different people on the soil, and those who were displaced
still fought to get it back. Those West Bank settlers would
never leave, I saw it in their eyes, and the Palestinians would
never be able to live with them. Three hundred years from
now they would still be fighting. You can slaughter a whole
generation, kill a mother in front of her child and eventually it
will be forgotten. But if you take land, the memory is fixed for
ever. Generations will look at the land and want it. They will
breed to fight. There was no love between tribes. Hate is so
accessible an emotion because we are already a species
swollen with it.

   I went to the Dead Sea, my final journey in Israel. The Dead
Sea is the lowest point on earth. I was drinking beer with
some backpackers on the beach when I saw her in the
distance. The great mound of flesh that was Sharon. I sat
with my back to her in case she recognized me. Soon we
were the only two people on the beach, and my curiosity got
the better of me. She was alone. I couldn't imagine where
Sandy was without her. As I approached she remained
motionless, staring out blankly over the sea to Jordan. I
hadn't thought of the Scottish girls much, I confess. I usually
only thought of myself. But wasn't everyone like that –
self-obsessed?

'Sharon?' I said. When she saw me she went wild. She hugged and kissed me and lifted me off my feet. I broke away from her and saw her face was smashed and bruised.

'What happened to you?'

'Och, Avril! Sandy has answered my prayers. She's looking oot for me still.'

'Where is she?'

'Avril. You will no' believe it. We were up north in a castle near the Syrian border. I think it's Syria up there. The guide told us we could crawl doon a staircase and come oot the side of a mountain. We thought that sounded like a laugh, you know? But we were going doon and doon and the stairs was all twisted and spiral like and broken and narrower and narrower and then we had to crawl on our knees through a tunnel. Avril, och, Avril. I was too fat and I'm closetphobic and I got stuck, and Sandy tried to get me to go back, but I screamed and shouted and kicked and she started to panic, too, and I started greeting, and then part of the tunnel fell. And I couldn't see her behind me, Avril. I crawled oot and I went back up to get her with the guide, but she was suffocated. Avril, Sandy was dead. We had to dig her oot. I killed Sandy. It was all my fault.' She blubbered and snotted into her hands. She looked at me in fright and demented hope, as if I would know the reason why people you loved and needed could be lost inside mountains.

'Avril. I'm all alone now. Ah cannae go on without her. She was all I had. I was all she had. But it was enough. I never asked for more than one person in the world to love me. It was lucky to get that. I pray to her now. Remember you said we had no gods, well, maybe she is up there for me now, do you think so? She sent you to me, didn't she? Help me, Avril. I've no money or food. I'm hungry.'

'You might lose some weight.'

'Avril, don't be mean to me. It's all true. I wish it wasn't. Avril, Sandy used to say you were a shite person with a great personality. But in the end she loved you as much as I did, didn't she, Avril?'

'I'm not running a popularity poll. Did this just happen? Is that why you're covered in bruises and bumps?'

'No. I've been by the sea a while. A week or two. Sandy's dead four months. These men wanted sex and I said I would if they took me to a restaurant. I swear my tummy was eating itself, all burning and acid. I was so hungry. They put me in their truck, and there were five of them, and they tied me up for two days and raped me. They fucken did. I swear to God. It was horrible. They beat the shite out of me with the handle of their guns. Look, Avril, ma front tooth has gone black.'

'Were they Arab or Israeli?'

'What does that matter, Avril? What the fuck does that matter?' She wailed like an animal. I glanced around nervously.

'I'm leaving Israel, Sharon. I called my parents and asked for the money to go home and they sent me so much I'm going to use it to go to India instead.'

Sharon snivelled and looked at me. Her eyelashes were all stuck together from her tears. 'I wish I had a ma and da to call. I don't even have the address of anyone anywhere. There was no one to even tell aboot Sandy. But won't your parents be sad you didn't come home?'

'They'll get over it.'

'Avril. I need to go home to Scotland. I cannae stand it any more here. Without Sandy there's nae telling what will happen to me. Could you just give me a wee loan? I'd pay it back, honestly. I'm in a bad way. I don't even have the bus fare away from this stupid sea. The men dumped me back here and told me to fuck off oot of Israel and never come back. I'm scared if they see me here they'll murder me, Avril. I've never been like this. You know that.'

It was true. Her happiness was well and truly drained. Her face, once so innocent, now looked puffy and angry. Any private moments of triumph that could light up her face from the inside were thoroughly extinguished.

'Remember I saved your life, Avril?'

I bristled. 'You can't drown in the Dead Sea, can you?'

'I don't know. I wasn't saying that for any reason. Just to remember what great friends we were.' She smiled at me. 'I'm so glad to see you. You were a good friend to Sandy and me. We got fired after you left. We felt so bad for bringing up your vomiting thingy. That was wrong. We were very sorry and we missed you badly.'

We talked on the rocky beach for another hour. She blabbered on and on nonsensically. I think she had lost what little she had of a mind. She begged me to hold her as she slept. Just for tonight. She was so afraid and so alone. Her grief was unbearable. A balloon of sorrow grown like a skin about the round planet, puffed up with diseased air, pushing against the atmosphere, never diminishing. It was so foul I could smell it. I lay beside her, throwing my thin arm like a snake about her broken bulk. A beached whale on the rocks. An emptied husk. Her snores echoed like trucks passing on the far road.

I rose and knelt beside her feet. She still wore the free kibbutz boots. I unlaced them gently and slipped them from her chubby feet. I swear she had stretch marks on her toes. Her nails had not been cut in months. They were thick, curled and yellow like rhinoceros horns. She stirred as I stood and whimpered in some lost sleeping fear. I filled the shoes with stones and walked them into the Dead Sea. The water was buoyant and it was hard to swim but I soaked the shoes entirely and struggled to make them sink. Then I ran back to her, grabbed my bag and stole away. I took a last look at the mountains of Jordan and the immense dead lick of a sea. I left her sleeping – a fat beaten thing, raped and poor, without even shoes to continue her journey, utterly alone.

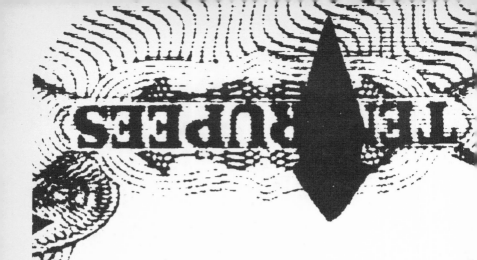

Simon Lewis

Justified and Ancient

Simon Lewis was born in 1971 in Wales and now lives in Brixton, south London. He has had stories published in the Pulp Faction anthologies Skin, Techno Pagan and Random Factor. His début novel Go was published in 1998. He is also the author of travel guides to

China

It was half a day's hike up the mountain to the village, and when they arrived Lee was exhausted. He wanted to get it over with and get back to Delhi as fast as possible, where, he fantasized, he would eat a giant plate of fried egg and chips, smothered in tomato sauce, and stay in a hotel with air conditioning. And from there he would get a train straight to Goa.

The village was a cluster of wooden huts fringing the summit. Lee waited outside while Punjee, his guide, entered to ask permission for the foreigner to come in. Lee sat on a rock in the shade and scratched his bites and worked out that he was thirty-seven kilometres from the nearest chocolate biscuit. All around, vertiginous peaks paraded off into the distance. Above, eagles circled in thermals. Below, a river mumbled through a shagpile carpeting of trees. The sun was bright, but it was cold in the shade and every breath felt like an iced drink. Lee lit a cigarette and played with his Zippo. Click flick, click. The only mechanical device he had seen all day, it seemed invested with significance, and its smooth operation was reassuring. Click flick, click.

'I have spoken to the village president,' said Punjee on his return. 'He will see you now. When we enter the village we must remember to be decorous. And – this is very important – you must not touch anything. Not the people or the cows or the houses.'

'Why?'

'Many things in the village are sacred, you understand? It is a holy place. A very old place.'

'How do I know what I can touch?'

'Don't touch anything unless it is given to you.'

Dark faces followed their progress along the narrow dirt

path that wound between the huts. A group of children, all hair and eyes and rags, pointed and giggled. Lee walked very close to Punjee, pacing like a detective, his hands in his pockets, eyes often cast downwards as if searching for clues. He noticed geometrical designs drawn on the ground in chalk. He flinched as a scruffy dog barked at him and returned the stare of a cow with painted horns which stood dumbly munching at the side of the track. He began to feel that his presence here was an anomaly, a freakish mistake, and he craved the familiar. There was nothing to indicate what century they were in, and he thought briefly of a film he liked as a kid, where some spaceman gets sent back to see King Arthur.

'This is a strange place,' said Punjee. 'The people are very isolated. They have their own traditions and customs. For example, if one villager has a dispute with another, they settle it by each poisoning a goat. The owner of the goat which dies first is the loser of the dispute.'

Lee spoke in a low whisper. 'What would happen if, say, I did touch something? By accident?'

'You would make people very upset.'

'Why?'

'You are an outsider, you understand? You are not pure.'

A young woman with a baby packaged on her back stepped into the long grass to let them pass. She was beautiful, and Lee studied her briefly, out of unconscious habit. She had big almond eyes, glowing skin and a slender frame she carried with effortless grace. She was barefoot, with thick silver bands around her ankles, and she carried a battered tin jug. Her face was impassive. She caught his eye briefly, then looked sharply aside.

'The women are very lovely, yes?' said Punjee. 'But they are also very proud. They would not look at you with your white skin and dirt.'

Though he resented the slight, Lee could not argue with Punjee's assessment of his appearance, which had deteriorated rapidly over the last few days as he had headed further into the mountains. His clothes were spattered with burrs and tears. Well, what could he do? There was no hot water anywhere.

They had come to an earth clearing. On one side stood a large wood-and-stone building, its surface alive with carved figures.

'Ah, now this is the temple,' said Punjee. 'Of course, you cannot go in here. You know, there is a silver statue of Vishnu inside, and every year . . .'

Lee wasn't listening. He was walking towards a hut opposite the temple, painted blue, with a line of empty cigarette packets strung above the door. He peered into the dark interior. A boy sat behind a wooden table, bobbing his head rhythmically up and down. A shelf on the wall beside him held a dusty collection of commodities. As Lee had suspected, it was a shop.

Lee stepped inside and scanned the shelf. Mostly it held bags of rice and tins of oil. Lee dived for a cluster of white-and-yellow packets stacked at one end.

'*We're justified*,' said the boy softly, '*and we're ancient.*' Biscuits! Lee grabbed Lemon Creams and Coconut Bites and turned to the boy. He realized that his bobbing was not, as he had assumed, some form of prayer; he was moving to music he could hear through the cheap headphones on his ears. He held a battered Walkman.

The boy continued singing. '*And we drive an ice cream va-an.*'

'I'll have these,' said Lee. He dug out his wallet and dropped two greasy, faded notes on the table. He was already tearing open the Lemon Creams as he left. He stuffed the other packet in his sweatshirt pocket.

Punjee was standing outside, talking to an old man.

'Biscuit?' mumbled Lee through a mouthful of crumbs. Punjee refused. To Lee's disappointment the Lemon Creams were revolting. He put the packet in his sweatshirt pocket and started on the Coconut Bites, which proved to be unpalatable. He looked at the packaging. They were six months out of date. He wondered what a class-three preservative was, then spat the gooey biscuit out.

'Lee,' said Punjee, 'I want you to meet the president of the village.'

'Welcome,' said the old man. His shapeless coat was draped over his thin shoulders as if on a coat hanger. Above it protruded a face so lined it reminded Lee of a raisin. His grey cap had a yellow flower tucked in it. He looked at Lee's mouth, flecked with crumbs. 'I see you have met my grandson. This way, please.' He led them towards a hut.

'The biscuits were brought up the mountain by Nepalese porters,' said Punjee. 'You remember, we saw some. Everything here has to be carried a long way.'

Lee remembered the porters. As he had gasped and staggered up a slope, a group of small men had skipped past with sacks on their backs, held by a band that went around their foreheads. Smiling and wearing flip-flops, they had looked like they were on holiday.

'In here.' The old man led them to a low doorway. Punjee kicked his trainers off, and Lee, following suit, removed his boots. The village president ushered them into the room beyond, a dark kitchen with the feel of a potting shed. The ceiling was too low for Lee, and he had to bow his head. Punjee and the old man squatted down by an earthen stove with a small, efficient fire burning underneath. Lee crouched awkwardly, his weight on the soles of his feet. He had seen Indians hold this posture for hours, but almost immediately his calves began to hurt.

The old man ladled milk and sugar into a metal pot over the stove and added leaves of tea and a sprinkling of spices. From the cavernous interior of his coat he withdrew a brown slab wrapped in Cellophane.

'This is cream.' He juggled the slab in his hand, then chucked it across at Lee. 'Try it.' Lee clawed at the Cellophane.

'So,' said Lee. 'How much –'

'My people want to know if you like our village.'

'Yeah, er, it's nice. Very ethnic.'

'It's a hard life in the mountains,' said Punjee. 'See how small the people are. They have no fat. But they are all muscle. They are strong people.' To demonstrate his assertion Punjee grabbed their host's arm and rolled his sleeve up, exposing a scrawny brown limb bumpy with muscles and tendons.

'Do you want to arm-wrestle?' said the old man.

'Oh, no, no,' said Lee, 'I am sure you would beat me.'

The old man began threading large hollow seeds from a tin beside him on to a strip of torn cotton. Lee took a chillum out of his pocket and began working fragments off the oily slab to put in it.

'What your country name?' he asked.

'England.'

'What your job?'

'In my country? Er, I don't really have one as such.'

'What your father do?'

'My father has a good job.' How could he tell these people what a management consultant was? 'He, er, he is in business,' said Lee.

The old man pointed at Lee and started counting on his fingers.

'I'm twenty-six,' said Lee.

'Married?'

'No.'

The village president pulled with his fingers at his short crop of grey hair, then pointed at Lee's pony-tail. He pursed his lips and fluttered his eyelashes and stuck his chin in the air.

'He thinks maybe you are a homosexual,' said Punjee.

'No,' said Lee. 'No no no. Me no gay. Many England people no marry.' Lee found himself enunciating clearly and adopting the grammatical style of his host. 'I have woman.' He pointed at his chest. 'I have many women. Not all at once, obviously. I mean, only one after the other, one at a time, yes? Now my woman in England. Linzi. Linzi good woman.

Well, sometimes. But Lee no marry Linzi. Linzi already have small baby. Little one not my son. Son of another man. Linzi was married. Now Linzi got divorce. Me and Linzi, good for a year, now not so good. Now I and Linzi have trial separation. I go back England, maybe I not want Linzi any more. Maybe she not want me. I don't know. But that's OK.' Aware that Punjee and the old man were looking at him with curiosity, Lee began to wind down. 'Then I go find a new woman. That's the way we do it. In my country. In England.'

Lee had no idea how much of his speech, if any, his audience understood. He began to feel stupid. He seemed unable to be natural with these people. He was ill at ease. The thick wad of notes in his moneybelt pressed into his stomach. The block of charas was so sticky it wouldn't break into crumbs. Still, it smelt very good. Lee wrapped a strip of cloth around the base and took out his Zippo.

The old man ladled tea into metal cups. With some solemnity he handed one to Lee.

Lee held the chillum up, and his host lit it for him. He puffed hard, screwing up his face.

'Is this not beautiful place?' said the old man with some pride. 'We have very good and simple life. And it gets better. You Westerners come here in your sunglasses with your hats and bring us money. We have doctor who comes now, maybe two times one month. This is good. Many children have problem, here' – he pointed at his eyes – 'and I try to get teacher for them.'

He leaned forward, smiling, as if to deliver a secret. 'Maybe one day we get electricity, and then satellite television.' He laughed loudly, throwing his mouth wide open. 'The earth is not good here. We have to work very hard for what we eat. The winter is bad. Sometimes we are cut off for many months. If you are not tough in mountains, you die. Of course, you know, there is one plant grows here no problem.'

Lee exhaled, filling the room with smoke.

'Good, yes? One kilo, yes? Only two thousand rupees,' said the old man.

'I'll give you a thousand,' said Lee, handing him the chillum and coughing. He soothed his raw throat with a swig of the sweet tea.

'No, no, you do not understand. Two thousand rupees is friend price.'

'Why are you giving me friend price?'

'Because you are with my good friend Punjee. Punjee's friend is my friend.'

The old man puffed and sucked and blew out a cloud.

'It's like I said, yes?' said Punjee. 'Is it not the best? You ask me to take you to where it is best, have I not done this? I think you take this to Goa, you can make really a lot of money.'

'It is a little expensive,' said Lee, 'I'll give you one thousand two hundred.'

'My friend, this is very low. Perhaps I would suggest one thousand eight hundred as reasonable price for you. Because I like your face. This is as low as I can go. Last price.'

'OK.'

Lee withdrew a wad of notes from his moneybelt and reminded himself of the relative modesty of the amount in sterling – barely twenty quid. And he could sell it on for a hundred times that. Indian money was joke money, small change, to anyone from one of the G7 nations. Lee had seen an American couple burst out laughing in a classy restaurant in Delhi, when a feast had worked out at a dollar a head. They couldn't believe their luck. They thought they'd died and gone to bargain heaven. A week's wages for a stone-breaker here might buy a packet of Smarties at home. Lee counted out eighteen brown hundred-rupee notes and handed them over. The money quickly disappeared into the coat.

'Everything is all right. Good business. Here is token.' The old man picked up the crude necklace of seeds he had made and tied the ends together. Gently he lifted it over Lee's head and arranged the seeds around his neck.

'Thank you,' Lee breathed, placing his hand on his chest like a bad actor being heartfelt. 'This means much to me.'

'Now we have sealed the trade in traditional way. I give you this as gesture of trust. To show you trust me, you give me this.'

He picked up Lee's Zippo, sitting on the uneven floor, and felt its weight.

'Wait, wait,' said Lee.

'You must not offend this man,' whispered Punjee.

'But –'

'A gesture of trust,' said the old man sharply. He flipped the lid and struck the wheel, watched the little djinn of flame for a second, then shut it up and slid it into his coat. He was all smiles again. Then he turned to Punjee and they started talking in Hindi in serious, low voices. Lee packed the charas into his day-sack and stumbled up. He wandered to the door, blinked at the light and put his boots on.

On the path outside two children pulled a third around in a small wooden cart. Lee caught the eye of the smallest child. Of indeterminate sex, it had one withered leg cocked out unnaturally at the knee and supported itself with the aid of a stick jutting out from its armpit. Lee smiled at it and the child grinned toothily back at him. Pleased, Lee gave it the packet of Coconut Bites. Immediately, the other bearer, a boy, dropped his rope, planted himself in front of Lee and thrust out a small hand. His fingers and palm were already etched and rough. The boy in the cart swivelled his raised head around, and Lee saw that he was blind, with pupilless eyes as white as cue-balls.

Lee gave the boys the Lemon Creams. His compassion towards these poor waifs touched him deeply, and Lee began to feel warm inside. The first child started tugging on Lee's jeans, shouting 'Rupee! Rupee!', and jumping up and down as best it could.

'No!' said Lee. 'Don't touch me! You shouldn't touch!'

The boy joined in, dancing around Lee's legs. Lee suddenly felt surrounded by thin brown limbs. 'Rupee, rupee!' The child on the cart turned his head towards the noise, smiled and shouted at the top of his voice, 'Rupee! Rupee!'

A young woman, barefoot and holding a broom, scooted from behind a house, shouted at the children, hit them one after the other and took away the packets of biscuits. Subdued, they abandoned their cart and sloped off down the track, the blind child led by the cripple. The woman glared at Lee.

Lee, embarrassed, stepped backwards into the hut, in time to see the old man hand Punjee a brown slab of charas. Punjee put it in an inside pocket of his jacket, then they stood up, shook hands and came outside. The village leader bade Punjee and Lee a cheery farewell, and waved.

Both men were silent as they walked back through the village. Lee relaxed into a mood of self-congratulation. The walk down to Jadi would be easy; he would sleep on a mattress tonight, in three days he would be talking to other dirty white people and matching MTV in cafés.

He wanted to leave the village quickly, and then maybe they would be back in Jadi, and its 'Last Stop Gusthose', by nightfall. Lee turned for one last look at the village, to consider from a safe distance the colourful people and their quaint little houses. From here the place looked quite attractive, the huts clinging to the mountain with lush greenery and rocks all around. It could be a picture on a postcard. The last villager they saw was a woman leading a donkey up towards the village. As she approached Lee recognized her as the girl he had seen earlier. He looked into her dark, silent face. Their eyes met, and then slid off, as they proceeded to their separate destinations.

Amrita slapped the back of the donkey, an old and useless animal which probably would not last the winter. The snow was coming early this year, a cause of much concern in the village. She turned and watched the retreating backs of the two men. The Englishman was very amusing. News of his arrival had preceded him, and many people had discussed his strange habits. He made such heavy, clumsy steps. Surely, she thought, such enormous shoes could not be comfortable? He looked very male with his thick, hairy arms and big neck, but he had a woman's hair hanging down his back. He had soft, fleshy hands that had never worked. He had hair on his face, but he did not grow a moustache so he had the look of a boy. He was big with food and hungry all the time. Not only did he clean himself with paper and then leave it lying around like a present for the next person, but he had been seen blowing his nose into a piece of cloth, which he had carefully folded up and put into his pocket, as if his own waste was of great value. He did not wash and keep himself clean, as a good person should; instead he sprayed a perfume on his body. His pink skin turned red in the sun. He was not suitably decorous to women.

Amrita felt sorry for the man, however rude and odd he was. Sometimes the president and his slimy friend Punjee got drunk and talked more than they should in the presence of the women. The president was a shrewd man, and under him the village knew a prosperity never previously dreamed of, but he was a man without honour. She knew the purpose of his visits to the town in the valley. She knew about his trips to see the police commissioner, Ram, in his concrete shed, and how the policeman gave him money in return for information. She knew that Ram and the bullies he used as deputies would be sitting getting drunk in Jadi now, and when the foreigner came down they would greet him, smiling, and Ram, proud in his green uniform, would laugh and stroke his waxed moustache, tapping his thick wooden cane against his leg.

Acknowledgements

Sarah would especially like to thank Simon Prosser, Lesley Shaw and Simon Trewin.

'A Representative in Automotive Components' copyright © Martyn Bedford, 1999; 'Prison Leave' copyright © Howard Marks, 1999; 'Shiprock' copyright © Helena Mulkerns, 1999; 'Such a Nice Time' copyright © Esther Freud, 1999; 'My Cold War: February 1998' copyright © Toby Litt, 1999; 'In the Union of Facelessness' copyright © Will Self, 1998, first published in the *New Statesman*; 'Bethlehem' copyright © Jean McNeil, 1999; 'My Kazakh Lover' copyright © Nicholas Blincoe, 1999; 'The Beasts of Marseille' copyright © John King, 1999; 'She Swallowed Her Pearls on the Day of the Revolution' copyright © Douglas Coupland, 1998, first published in *Wallpaper*; 'Horizontal Drift' copyright © Geoff Dyer, 1999; 'We're Here, Anderson Says' copyright © Emily Perkins, 1999; 'The Institute' copyright © William Sutcliffe, 1999; 'It was the 90s' copyright © Grant Morrison, 1999; 'Oh to Play Golf on Mars' copyright © James Flint, 1999; 'A Sacrificial Shoe' copyright © Emer Martin, 1999; 'Justified and Ancient' copyright © Simon Lewis, 1999

FARE

TAX

TOTAL

FARE CALCULATION

E OF THE
APPEA THE C

MAN

24B

535

CONTENT • CONTENU • INHALT